SCOTLAND'S BOOKSHELF
A celebration of 100 years of Scottish writing

With an introduction by Rosemary Goring

This selection published in Great Britain in 2012 for the
Aye Write! Book Festival by Glasgow Libraries
The Mitchell Library, 201 North Street, Glasgow G3 7DN
Tel: 0141 287 2999 · www.glasgowlife.org.uk/libraries

A CIP catalogue record for this book is
available from the British Library.

ISBN 978 0 90616 971 1

Printed and bound by CPI Group (UK) Ltd, Croydon, CR0 4YY

CONTENTS

SCOTLAND'S BOOKSHELF: an introduction   7
by Rosemary Goring

1911-1919   10
PETER AND WENDY by J. M. Barrie (1911)   12
THE THIRTY-NINE STEPS by John Buchan (1915)   14

1920-1929   18
A DRUNK MAN LOOKS AT THE THISTLE   20
by Hugh MacDiarmid (1926)
DARK STAR by Lorna Moon (1929)   24

1930-1939   27
HATTER'S CASTLE by A J. Cronin (1931)   29
SUNSET SONG by Lewis Grassic Gibbon (1932)   31

1940-1949   34
THE SILVER DARLINGS by Neil M. Gunn (1941)   36
DÀIN DO EIMHIR AGUS DÀIN EILE (Poems to Eimhir   39
and Other Poems) by Somhairle MacGill-Eain
(Sorley MacLean) (1943)

1950-1959   44
YOUNG ADAM by Alexander Trocchi (1954)   46
THE CONE GATHERERS by Robin Jenkins (1955)   48

1960-1969   51
THE PRIME OF MISS JEAN BRODIE by Muriel Spark (1961)   53
A HISTORY OF THE SCOTTISH PEOPLE 1560-1830   55
by T. C. Smout (1969)

1970-1979   58
GREENVOE by George Mackay Brown (1972)   60
DOCHERTY by William McIlvanney (1975)   62

1980-1989   65
THE WASP FACTORY by Iain Banks (1984)   67
A QUESTION OF LOYALTIES by Allan Massie (1989)   69

1990-1999   73
SWING HAMMER SWING! by Jeff Torrington (1992)   75
TRAINSPOTTING by Irvine Welsh (1993)   77

2000-2011   81
CLARA by Janice Galloway (2002)   83
GIRL MEETS BOY by Ali Smith (2007)   85

A LONGLIST OF SCOTTISH WRITING   88

SCOTLAND'S BOOKSHELF: *an introduction by Rosemary Goring*
(Literary Editor, Herald and Times Group)

Last November Glasgow's magnificent Mitchell Library celebrated its 100th anniversary at Charing Cross. Although the bequest of the tobacco manufacturer Stephen Mitchell first opened in 1877 on the corner of Ingram Street and Albion Street, it is in its current location, looking down on the roaring M8 traffic, that it has made a name as one of the foremost reference libraries in Europe.

To celebrate its venerable history, Karen Cunningham, Head of Glasgow Libraries and Director of Aye Write! festival, had the idea of choosing two of the best books published each decade across the past century, and selecting extracts from each of them to make a volume for the library's annual free city read programme, which for the first time ever will be available in libraries across all of Scotland. This sampler is intended to give a flavour of the range of literary treasure the Mitchell Library, and Scotland, has witnessed in one hundred years – to provide, in effect, a shorthand guide to some of the most influential books from that period that should sit on everyone's bookshelf, whether that shelf is real or simply in one's head.

Karen Cunningham gathered a judging panel comprising some of the most eager and greedy readers in the city: Professor Willy Maley from Glasgow University, and herself, Susan Taylor and Mary Greenshields from Glasgow Libraries. She asked me, as Literary Editor of The Herald and Sunday Herald, to be chair.

Lists, of course, can cause trouble. In fact, they usually do. Thankfully the discussions were good-humoured, so I didn't have to raise my voice, or thump a gavel. This is not to say, however, that making this selection was easy. It was almost impossible. A quick glance at works published by Scots between 1911 and 2011 shows that this exercise is very subjective. There is no right or wrong top twenty best books for this period, just various lists according to varying tastes. A mathematician could no doubt calculate how many versions of the list are possible, but not having a head for numbers, and finding twenty more than enough to cope with, I'd rather not know. Certainly a different panel might have come up with entirely different books, all of them – or almost all of them – as significant and representative as those we've chosen. So for any who shake their heads at our inclusions, who mourn our omissions, or think this task was child's play, we include lists of some of the main titles we were choosing from at the back of this book.

From the start we restricted our choice to fiction, poetry, children's books and non-fiction. Only one book per author could make the final selection, even though many writers, such as Muriel Spark, or Sorley MacLean, had major books published in more than one decade. There are also two significant but deliberate gaps: Alasdair Gray is not on the list because last year Glasgow Libraries published a chapter of Lanark as their city read, to mark the novel's 30th anniversary, and it was felt inappropriate to include him again. James Kelman, one of Scotland's foremost writers, and the country's only Booker Prize winner, is also not here, having asked not to be included.

What follows is the tip of the iceberg. The literary pinnacles we have picked out will still, we feel sure, be read and appreciated in a hundred years' time. Some currently beneath the waterline will be reassessed in the future and find renewed popularity, while others will no doubt sink without trace for ever.

A century of Scottish writing is a long time. It is thanks to the inspiration of the authors chosen here, and the very many others not included, that the Mitchell Library has become such a national landmark. It is not just the library, however, but countless thousands of readers within its walls, past and present, who have been shaped by a hundred years of solitary reading.

Rosemary Goring,
January 2012

1911-1919

PETER AND WENDY (1911) *by J. M. Barrie*
THE THIRTY-NINE STEPS (1915) *by John Buchan*

In the early years of the 20th century, the influence of the fading Victorian era was still very obvious. Playwright J. M. Barrie came out of the sentimental kailyard tradition that coloured a great deal of Scotland's fiction towards the end of the 19th century. Nobody could say, however, that *Peter and Wendy*, the novel version of his play *Peter Pan*, which had taken London by storm in 1904 and has been a favourite ever since, is in any way sugary or twee. A magical, timeless and in many ways disturbing story about a little boy called Peter Pan who will not grow up, and entices innocent young playmates to join him in his adventures, it nevertheless has a psychological acuteness and a sinister undertow that is very modern. With wit, invention and charm, Barrie's *Peter and Wendy* catapults a netherworld of fairies and fantastical characters into a contemporary setting, namely wealthy turn of the century Kensington, and gives an impish twist to a tale whose roots lie deep in the old country's fairy-story tradition.

John Buchan's *The Thirty-Nine Steps* is a world away from Barrie's children's fantasy, yet it shares the same love of high adventure. Set in 1914, when Europe is on the brink of war, it's the story of Richard Hannay, an adventurous expat Scot recently returned to London from South Africa, who stumbles on a German conspiracy to kill the president of Greece. When the spy who has told him of this plot is murdered in Hannay's flat, the Scot is forced to flee to the Scottish hills as he seeks out the truth, all the while avoiding his pursuers. Buchan wrote this novel while recovering from an ulcer. Its title, his son later revealed, came from the nursing home in Broadstairs where he was recuperating: "There was a wooden staircase leading down to the beach. My sister, who was about six, and who had just learnt to count properly, went down them and gleefully announced: there are Thirty-Nine steps."

Novels and works from the same time as these two books include Arthur Conan Doyle's science-fiction fantasy, *The Lost World* (1912), in which a gung-ho journalist discovers prehistoric creatures in a remote Amazonian plateau, a theme picked up by several subsequent writers, from Edgar Rice Burroughs's *The Land that Time Forgot*, to Michael Crichton's *Jurassic Park*. Conan Doyle may have got the idea himself from Jules Verne's *Journey to the Centre of the Earth*.

History, both factual and fictional dominates the other major works of the period, among them the prolific historian Andrew Lang's vivid *A Short History of Scotland (1911)*, *The New Road* (1914), a thriller by Neil Munro set in 1733, around the notorious road built by General Wade in the Highlands, and historical novelist and poet Violet Jacob's *Flemington* (1911), set at the time of the '45 Jacobite rebellion. John Buchan considered this "the best Scots romance since *The Master of Ballantrae*." Most enduring of all, perhaps, is John Macdougall Hay's deeply dark novel *Gillespie* (1914), a haunting, hallucinatory story which was hailed as brilliant by Thomas Hardy. Its depiction of one man's relentless pursuit of power is still, sadly, familiar and fresh.

Rosemary Goring,
January 2012

PETER AND WENDY *by J. M. Barrie*

We now return to the nursery.

'It's all right,' John announced, emerging from his hiding-place. 'I say, Peter, can you really fly?'

Instead of troubling to answer him Peter flew round the room, taking the mantelpiece on the way.

'How topping!' said John and Michael.

'How sweet!' cried Wendy.

'Yes, I'm sweet, oh, I am sweet!' said Peter, forgetting his manners again.

It looked delightfully easy, and they tried it first from the floor and then from the beds, but they always went down instead of up.

'I say, how do you do it?' asked John, rubbing his knee. He was quite a practical boy.

'You just think lovely wonderful thoughts,' Peter explained, 'and they lift you up in the air.'

He showed them again.

'You're so nippy at it,' John said; 'couldn't you do it very slowly once?'

Peter did it both slowly and quickly. 'I've got it now, Wendy!' cried John, but soon he found he had not. Not one of them could fly an inch, though even Michael was in words of two syllables, and Peter did not know A from Z.

Of course Peter had been trifling with them, for no one can fly unless the fairy dust has been blown on him. Fortunately, as we have mentioned, one of his hands was messy with it, and he blew some on each of them, with the most superb results.

'Now just wriggle your shoulders this way,' he said, 'and let go.'

They were all on their beds, and gallant Michael let go first. He did not quite mean to let go, but he did it, and immediately he was borne across the room.

'I flewed!' he screamed while still in midair.

John let go and met Wendy near the bathroom.

'Oh, lovely!'

'Oh, ripping!'

'Look at me!'

'Look at me!'

'Look at me!'

They were not nearly so elegant as Peter, they could not help kicking a little, but their heads were bobbing against the ceiling, and there is almost nothing so delicious as that. Peter gave Wendy a hand at first, but had to desist, Tink was so indignant.

Up and down they went, and round and round. Heavenly was Wendy's word.

'I say,' cried John, 'why shouldn't we all go out!'

Of course it was to this that Peter had been luring them.

Michael was ready: he wanted to see how long it took him to do a billion miles. But Wendy hesitated.

'Mermaids!' said Peter again.

'Oo!'

'And there are pirates.'

'Pirates,' cried John, seizing his Sunday hat, 'let us go at once.'

It was just at this moment that Mr. and Mrs. Darling hurried with Nana out of 27. They ran into the middle of the street to look up at the nursery window; and, yes, it was still shut, but the room was ablaze with light, and most heart-gripping sight of all, they could see in shadow on the curtain three little figures in night attire circling round and round, not on the floor but in the air.

Not three figures, four!

In a tremble they opened the street door. Mr. Darling would have rushed upstairs, but Mrs. Darling signed to him to go softly. She even tried to make her heart go softly.

Will they reach the nursery in time? If so, how delightful for them, and we shall all breathe a sigh of relief, but there will be no story. On the other hand, if they are not in time, I solemnly promise that it will all come right in the end.

They would have reached the nursery in time had it not been that the little stars were watching them. Once again the stars blew the window open, and that smallest star of all called out:

'Cave, Peter!'

Then Peter knew that there was not a moment to lose. 'Come,' he cried imperiously, and soared out at once into the night, followed by John and Michael and Wendy.

Mr. and Mrs. Darling and Nana rushed into the nursery too late. The birds were flown.

From Peter and Wendy by J. M. Barrie

THE THIRTY-NINE STEPS *by John Buchan*

The station, when I reached it, proved to be ideal for my purpose. The moor surged up around it and left room only for the single line, the slender siding, a waiting-room, an office, the stationmaster's cottage, and a tiny yard of gooseberries and sweet-william. There seemed no road to it from anywhere, and to increase the desolation the waves of a tarn lapped on their grey granite beach half a mile away. I waited in the deep heather till I saw the smoke of an east-going train on the horizon. Then I approached the tiny booking-office and took a ticket for Dumfries.

The only occupants of the carriage were an old shepherd and his dog - a wall-eyed brute that I mistrusted. The man was asleep, and on the cushions beside him was that morning's *Scotsman*. Eagerly I seized on it, for I fancied it would tell me something.

There were two columns about the Portland Place Murder, as it was called. My man Paddock had given the alarm and had the milkman arrested. Poor devil, it looked as if the latter had earned his sovereign hardly; but for me he had been cheap at the price, for he seemed to have occupied the police for the better part of the day. In the latest news I found a further instalment of the story. The milkman had been released, I read, and the true criminal, about whose identity the police were reticent, was believed to have got away from London by one of the northern lines. There was a short note about me as the owner of the flat. I guessed the police had stuck that in, as a clumsy contrivance to persuade me that I was unsuspected.

There was nothing else in the paper, nothing about foreign politics or Karolides, or the things that had interested Scudder. I laid it down, and found that we were approaching the station at which I had got out yesterday. The potato-digging stationmaster had been gingered up into some activity, for the west-going train was waiting to let us pass, and from it had descended three men who were asking him questions. I supposed that they were the local police, who had been stirred up by Scotland Yard, and had traced me as far as this one-horse siding. Sitting well back in the shadow I watched them carefully. One of them had a book, and took down notes. The old potato-digger seemed to have turned peevish, but the child who had collected my ticket was talking volubly. All the party looked out across the moor where the white road departed. I hoped they were going to take up my tracks there.

As we moved away from that station my companion woke up. He fixed me with a wandering glance, kicked his dog viciously, and inquired where he was. Clearly he was very drunk.

'That's what comes o' bein' a teetotaller,' he observed in bitter regret.

I expressed my surprise that in him I should have met a blue-ribbon stalwart.

"Ay, but I'm a strong teetotaller," he said pugnaciously. "I took the pledge last Martinmas, and I havena touched a drop o' whisky sinsyne. Not even at Hogmanay, though I was sair temptit."

He swung his heels up on the seat, and burrowed a frowsy head into the cushions.

"And that's a' I get," he moaned. "A heid hetter than hell fire, and twae een lookin' different ways for the Sabbath."

"What did it?" I asked.

"A drink they ca' brandy. Bein' a teetotaller I keepit off the whisky, but I was nip-nippin' a' day at this brandy, and I doubt I'll no be weel for a fortnicht." His voice died away into a stutter, and sleep once more laid its heavy hand on him.

My plan had been to get out at some station down the line, but the train suddenly gave me a better chance, for it came to a standstill at the end of a culvert which spanned a brawling porter-coloured river. I looked out and saw that every carriage window was closed and no human figure appeared in the landscape. So I opened the door, and dropped quickly into the tangle of hazels which edged the line.

It would have been all right but for that infernal dog. Under the impression that I was decamping with its master's belongings, it started to bark, and all but got me by the trousers. This woke up the herd, who stood bawling at the carriage door in the belief that I had committed suicide. I crawled through the thicket, reached the edge of the stream, and in cover of the bushes put a hundred yards or so behind me. Then from my shelter I peered back, and saw the guard and several passengers gathered round the open carriage door and staring in my direction. I could not have made a more public departure if I had left with a bugler and a brass band.

Happily the drunken herd provided a diversion. He and his dog, which was attached by a rope to his waist, suddenly cascaded out of the carriage, landed on their heads on the track, and rolled some way down the bank towards the water. In the rescue which followed the dog bit somebody, for I could hear the sound of hard swearing. Presently they had forgotten me, and when after a quarter of a mile's crawl I ventured to look back, the train had started again and was vanishing in the cutting.

I was in a wide semicircle of moorland, with the brown river as radius, and the high hills forming the northern circumference. There was not a sign or sound of a human being, only the plashing water and the interminable crying of curlews. Yet, oddly enough, for the first time I felt the terror of the hunted on me. It was not the police that I thought of, but the other folk, who knew that I knew Scudder's secret and dared not let me live. I was certain that they would pursue me with a keenness and vigilance unknown to the British law, and that once their grip closed on me I should find no mercy.

I looked back, but there was nothing in the landscape. The sun glinted on the metals of the line and the wet stones in the stream, and you could not have found a more peaceful sight in the world. Nevertheless I started to run. Crouching low in the runnels of the bog, I ran till the sweat blinded my eyes. The mood did not leave me till I had reached the rim of mountain and flung myself panting on a ridge high above the young waters of the brown river.

From my vantage-ground I could scan the whole moor right away to the railway line and to the south of it where green fields took the place of heather. I have eyes like a hawk, but I could see nothing moving in the whole countryside. Then I looked east beyond the ridge and saw a new kind of landscape - shallow green valleys with plentiful fir plantations and the faint lines of dust which spoke of highroads. Last of all I looked into the blue May sky, and there I saw that which set my pulses racing...

From *The Thirty-Nine Steps* by John Buchan

1920-1929

A DRUNK MAN LOOKS AT THE THISTLE (1926) *by Hugh MacDiarmid* DARK STAR (1929) *by Lorna Moon*

One 20th-century Scottish book towers above readers, and writers, like a giant. It was not only a work of literary genius, but it dragged Scottish letters and, arguably, Scotland itself, into the modern era. *A Drunk Man Looks at the Thistle* by C. M. Grieve, writing under his lifelong pseudonym of Hugh MacDiarmid, is a magnificently profound and ambitious poem, whose presence hovers over every writer whose language is Scots, and every citizen who cares about Scotland's cultural and spiritual identity.

Surely the thistliest, prickliest literary figure Scotland has ever produced, MacDiarmid wrote his epic first-person poem in the persona of a drunk lying on a hillside, beneath the moonlight, and contemplating not just his own navel, but that of the nation too. It has been considered by some critics to be the equal of T. S. Eliot's *The Wasteland*, and certainly it was the first true blast of modernism from Scotland, overtaking many English and Irish authors to lead the vanguard of modernist expression. What distinguishes MacDiarmid's *Drunk Man* from much of the work of his peers – the likes of Yeats, and Eliot and Ezra Pound – is his confidence, humour and sense of optimism, a cast of mind that few would have associated with Scotland from its literature up to that point.

Dark Star by contrast still clings to old-fashioned, traditional Scotland. This is in some ways odd, given that its author, Lorna Moon, a beautiful, acerbic freespirit from Strichen in Aberdeenshire, had kicked over the traces of small-town life and absconded, first for Canada with a travelling salesman, and then to Hollywood. There she became a writer and had a son by Cecil B. DeMille's brother, before dying young from tuberculosis. *Dark Star* is a melodramatic, sometimes unconvincing romance in which an illegitimate girl, called Nancy, living in the north east as had Moon, goes in search of her parents, and in so doing finds love. Moon was a tart critic of her homeland, and here, as in her short story collection, *Doorways in Drumorty*, she pokes fun at the hypocrisies of the narrow-minded land she had left behind. This novel stands out as a rare blast for its times on behalf of female independence and sexual honesty. As Moon wrote, it was a "sincere effort to show what the men in a woman's life bring to her, and take from her ... It is the inside of a woman written from the inside."

The twenties saw an outpouring of women's writing, and other contenders for the bookshelf list included the lyrical Nan Shepherd's novel *The Quarry Wood* (1928), about a feisty girl from a poor Deeside family, kailyard novelist Annie Shepherd Swan's *Closed Doors* (1926), and most interesting of all, writer and critic Catherine Carswell's semi-autobiographical novel of Edwardian Glasgow, *Open the Door!* (1920), which is a clear-eyed account of an intelligent young woman's bid for autonomy.

Rosemary Goring,
January 2012

A DRUNK MAN LOOKS AT THE THISTLE *by Hugh MacDiarmid*

Our universe is like an ee
Turned in, man's benmaist hert to see,
And swamped in subjectivity.

But whether it can use its sicht
To bring what lies without to licht
To answer's still ayont my micht.

But when that inturned look has brocht
To licht what still in vain it's socht
Outward maun be the bent o thocht.

And organs may develop sune
Responsive to the need divine
O single-minded humankind.

The function, as it seems to me,
O' Poetry is to bring to be
At lang, lang last that unity...

But wae's me on the weary wheel!
Higgledy-piggledy in't we reel,
And little it cares hou we may feel.

Twenty-six thousand years 't'll tak
For it to threid the Zodiac
—A single round o' the wheel to mak!

Lately it turned—I saw mysel
In sic a company doomed to mell,
I micht hae been in Dante's Hell.

It shows hou little the best o men
E'en o themsels at times can ken,
—I sune saw that when I gaed ben

The lesser wheel within the big
That moves as merry as a grig,
Wi mankind in its whirligig,

And hasna turned ae circle yet
Tho as it turns we slide in it,
And needs maun tak the place we get,

I felt it turn, and syne I saw
John Knox and Clavers in my raw,
And Mary Queen o Scots anaa,

And Rabbie Burns and Weelum Wallace,
And Carlyle lookan unco gallus,
And Harry Lauder (to enthrall us).

And as I looked I saw them aa,
Aa the Scots baith big and smaa,
That e'er the braith o life did draw,

"Mercy o Gode, I canna thole
Wi sic an orra mob to roll."
—"*Wheesht! It's for the guid o your soul.*"

"But what's the meanin, what's the sense?"
— "*Men shift but by experience.
Twixt Scots there is nae difference.*

*They canna learn, sae canna move,
But stick for aye to their auld groove
—The only race in History who've*

*Bidden in the same category
Frae stert to present o their story,
And deem their ignorance their glory.*

*The mair they differ, mair the same.
The wheel can whummle aa but them,
—They caa their obstinacy "Hame,"*

*And 'Puir Auld Scotland' bleat wi pride,
And wi their minds made up to bide
A thorn in aa the wide world's side.*

There hae been Scots wha hae haen thochts,
They're strewn through maist o the various lots
—Sic traitors are nae langer Scots!"'

"But in this huge ineducable
Heterogeneous hotch and rabble,
Why am *I* condemned to squabble?"

"A Scottish poet maun assume
The burden o his people's doom,
And dee to brak their livan tomb.

Mony hae tried, but aa hae failed.
Their sacrifice has nocht availed.
Upon the thistle they're impaled.

You maun choose but gin ye'd see
Anither category ye
Maun tine your nationality."

And I look at aa the random
Band the wheel leaves whaur it fand 'em
                  "Auch, to Hell,
I'll tak' it to avizandum." ...

O wae's me on the weary wheel,
And fain I'd understand them!

And blessin on the weary wheel,
Whaurever it may land them! ...

But aince Jean kens what I've been through
The nicht, I dinna dout it,
She'll ope her airms in welcome true,
And clack nae mair about it ...

*   *   *   *   *   *

The stars like thistle's roses flouer
The sterile growth o Space outour,

That clad in bitter blasts spreids out
Frae me, the sustenance o its root.

O fain I'd keep my hert entire,
Fain hain the licht o my desire,
But ech! the shinean streams ascend,
And leave me empty at the end.

For aince it's toomed my hert and brain,
The thistle needs maun faa again.
—But aa its growth 'll never fill
The hole it's turned my life intill! ...

Yet hae I Silence left, the croun o aa.

No her, wha on the hills langsyne I saw
Liftan a foreheid o perpetual snaw.

No her, wha in the how-dumb-deid o nicht
Kyths, like Eternity in Time's despite.

No her, withouten shape, whas name is Daith,
No Him, unkennable abies to faith

— God whom, gin e'er He saw a man, wad be
E'en mair dumfounerd at the sicht than he.

—But Him, whom nocht in man or Deity,
Or Daith or Dreid or Laneliness can touch,
Wha's deed owre often and has seen owre much.

O I hae Silence left ,
          —"And weel ye micht,"
Sae Jean'll say, "efter sic a nicht!"

THE END

*From A Drunk Man Looks at the Thistle by Hugh MacDiarmid, published
by Polygon, an imprint of Birlinn Ltd, and reprinted by kind permission.*

DARK STAR *by Lorna Moon*

She could not remember when she had been first taken to Rossorty. But she would never forget the first time she had looked on it, with eyes that saw its beauty.

On sunny days its one narrow street ran straight up the rose-coloured cliff into the sky. On dull days it had a gentler, less dramatic beauty. But never could it look like any other town.

Great rose-coloured cliffs, without a blade of green, sloped up like a reclining wall shutting off the sea, and up this rosy slope, almost to its top, marched the lime-white little cottages. The blue of the sky, the rose of the street, the white of the houses, with their yellow thatched bonnets, and, like veils upon their faces, the nets hanging to dry; nothing ever looked just like that. The seaward side was one sheer drop against which the ocean dashed and roared, eating inward in great caverns. At low tide it rolled away to show the ancient smuggling caves of the Fasseferns. But when the tide was high it sent its spray flying to the cliff-top, and the sunlight made of it a rainbow diadem to crown Rossorty.

It was on such a day that it first pierced her with its wonder. In one sharp moment she saw, and never would forget. Nothing that went before was clear, but suddenly, into the half-dark that is the narrow vision of a child, there flashed, with the clatter of hoofs, this blaze of beauty...

Past her up the street rode a man, madly spurring his horse, his bare white head shining like silk, in scarlet hunting-coat and white breeches, astride an ash-white horse, and down its slender flanks the blood was trickling.

Up, up the steep street he rode, lashing the horse, and as he passed, women rushed to their doors and children scampered away.

On, on, up the rose path toward the rainbow mist.

To the top, and out of sight!

A scream went up as if from one despairing throat. And then they ran, following his path; fleet young women with children in their arms; ponderous, heavy-footed mothers of men; grey-haired grandmothers wailing toothlessly, and hobbling old men; and with them ran Nancy.

Cries and wailing everywhere: "Another Fassefern gone to his death. Suicide Fasseferns! Suicide Fasseferns! Ill luck to Rossorty and our men at sea. Woe, woe, the day!"

At the top they threw themselves upon the ground and crept forward to the cliff's sharp edge, gazing down upon the lashing coiling water. Nothing could be seen of horse or man; only the sea continuing its age-old programme, hissing up the time-worn rocks, then drawing in its breath to hiss again more wildly.

But while grey heads stared down, despairing at the sharp black teeth of the sea, Nancy looked upward, expecting to see horse and rider galloping in the blue above. For never could she quite believe that he had not ridden straight into the sky. And the beauty of this mad thing was for ever stamped upon her soul.

From Dark Star by Lorna Moon.

1930-1939

HATTER'S CASTLE (1931) *by A. J. Cronin*
SUNSET SONG (1932) *by Lewis Grassic Gibbon*

The growing political and economic gloom of the late 1920s and 1930s were already making themselves felt on this decade's fiction, and titles such as Dot Allan's novel *Hunger March* (1934), George Blake's *The Shipbuilders* (1935) and H. Kingsley Long and Alexander McArthur's *No Mean City: A Story of the Glasgow Slums* (1935), need no explanation, while James Barke's *The Land of the Leal* (1939) moves from the Victorian countryside to Depression-era Glasgow. Both the choices for this decade, however, are set in earlier eras, the first from around the time of the Tay Bridge disaster, the second from the turn of the century and including World War One. It is likely, nevertheless, that the gathering darkness across Europe influenced the imaginations of these two novelists as much as those who wrote on more current affairs.

Hatter's Castle was the debut of doctor A. J. Cronin. The story of the ulcer's role in the history of Scottish fiction has still to be written, but its part is substantial for Cronin, like John Buchan before him, wrote his life-changing novel while recuperating from this ailment. *Hatter's Castle* was so successful, he never lifted a stethoscope again.

No claims can be made for this novel's subtlety. A piece of gothic misery that makes the Greek tragedians look cheerful, it might be dismissed as pure melodrama were it not so powerfully and believably executed. Cronin's professional life, one suspects, furnished more than a few details of the trapped characters he portrays. Once read, it is never forgotten, though with a shudder at the memory of Cronin's portrait of a monstrously cruel father who one by one destroys the lives of his two daughters and wife.

James Leslie Mitchell, who wrote under the name Lewis Grassic Gibbon, was a very different kind of novelist. *Sunset Song*, the first of his *A Scots' Quair* trilogy, which continues with *Cloud Howe* (1933) and *Grey Granite* (1934), was written in a frantic burst of energy in less than two months. The pressure Grassic Gibbon put himself under to write all three novels, and four other books beside in the space of only two years is considered by some as the reason for his most untimely death in 1935 at the age of 34, following a perforated ulcer.

Set in Grassic Gibbon's native heath of the Mearns, in the north-east, *Sunset Song* is the tale of young Chris Guthrie, a crofter's daughter who experiences the full brutality of life when her mother commits suicide rather than face another pregnancy. Thereafter her father grows increasingly aggressive towards his children. Chris is one of the finest literary characters to come out of Scotland, and her story is followed through the trilogy to its bitter end. In this novel, Grassic Gibbon is more lyrical and elegaic than in his later books, which may explain its huge popularity. His heroine's bone-deep love of her homeland is a mirror of the author's. As she reflects, in a typically heart-felt moment: "the land was forever, it moved and changed below you, but was forever, you were close to it and it to you, not at a bleak remove it held you and hurted you. And she had thought to leave it all!"

Rosemary Goring,
January 2012

HATTER'S CASTLE *by A. J. Cronin*

James Brodie awoke next morning with the sun streaming in
through his window. He had especially designated this room at
the back of the house as his bedroom because, with an animal
appreciation of sunshine, he loved the bright morning rays to strike
in and waken him, to soak through the blankets into his receptive
body, and saturate his being with a sense of power and radiance.
"There's no sun like the morning sun," was one of his favourite
sayings, one of his stock of apparently profound axioms which he
drew upon largely in his conversation and repeated with a knowing
and astute air. "The mornin' sun's the thing! We don't get enough o'
it, but in MY room I've made sure o' all that's goin'."

He yawned largely and stretched his massive frame luxuriously,
observed with half-opened yet appreciative eyes the golden swarm
of motes that swam around him, then, after a moment, blinked
questioningly towards the clock on the mantelpiece, the hands
of which marked only eight o'clock; becoming aware that he had
another quarter of an hour in bed, he put his head down, rolled
over on his side, and dived beneath the blankets like a gigantic
porpoise. But soon he came up again. Despite the beauty of the
morning, despite the brosy odour of the boiling porridge which his
wife was preparing downstairs and which, arising, gently titillated
his nostrils, his present humour lacked the full complacency which
he felt it should have held.

Moodily, as though seeking the cause of his discontent, he
turned and surveyed the hollow on the other side of the big bed,
which his wife had left a full hour ago when, according to custom,
she had arisen in good time to have everything in order and his
breakfast ready upon the table the moment he came down. What
good, he reflected resentfully, was a woman like that to a man
like him? She might cook, wash, scrub, darn his socks, brush his
boots, aye, and lick his boots too; but what kind of armful was she
now? Besides, since her last confinement, when she had borne
him Nessie, she had been always ailing, in a weak, whining way,
offending his robust vigour by her flaccid impotence and provoking
his distaste by her sickly habits. Out of the corner of his eye when
she thought herself unobserved, as in the early hours of the
morning when she left the bed before him, he would contemplate
her almost stealthy dressing with disgust. Only last Sunday he
had detected her in the act of concealing some soiled garment,

and had roared at her like an angry ram: "Don't make a midden of my bedroom! It's bad enough for me to put up with you without havin' your dirty clothes flung in my face!" She had, he considered bitterly, long since been repugnant to him; the very smell of her was obnoxious to him, and had he not been a decent man, he might well have looked elsewhere. What had he dreamed last night? He thrust out his lower lip longingly and stretched his legs powerfully as he played with the vision of his sleep, thinking of the tantalising young jade he had chased through the woods who, though he had run like a stag, had been saved by the fleetness of her foot. She had run, faster than a deer, her long hair flying behind her, and with not a stitch on her back to cumber her, but still, despite her speed, had turned to smile at him enticingly, provokingly. If he had only gotten a grip of her, he thought, allowing his erotic fancy to riot delightfully as he lay back, basking his ponderous body in the sun, his parted lips twitching with a half-lewd, half-sardonic amusement, he would have made her pipe to a different tune.

From Hatter's Castle by A. J. Cronin (Copyright © A. J. Cronin, 1931) reprinted by kind permission of A.M. Heath & Co. Ltd

SUNSET SONG *by Lewis Grassic Gibbon*

THE SONG

Ploughing

Below and around where Chris Guthrie lay the June moors whispered and rustled and shook their cloaks, yellow with broom and powdered faintly with purple, that was the heather but not the full passion of its colour yet. And in the east against the cobalt blue sky lay the shimmer of the North Sea, that was by Bervie, and maybe the wind would veer there in an hour or so and you'd feel the change in the life and strum of the thing, bringing a streaming coolness out of the sea. But for days now the wind had been in the south, it shook and played in the moors and went dandering up the sleeping Grampians, the rushes pecked and quivered about the loch when its hand was upon them, but it brought more heat than cold, and all the parks were fair parched, sucked dry, the red clay soil of Blawearie gaping open for the rain that seemed never-coming. Up here the hills were brave with the beauty and the heat of it, but the hayfield was all a crackling dryness and in the potato park beyond the biggings the shaws drooped red and rusty already. Folk said there hadn't been such a drought since eighty-three and Long Rob of the Mill said you couldn't blame *this* one on Gladstone, anyway, and everybody laughed except father, God knows why.

Some said the North, up Aberdeen way, had had rain enough, with Dee in spate and bairns hooking stranded salmon down in the shallows, and that must be fine enough, but not a flick of the greeve weather had come over the hills, the roads you walked down to Kinraddie smithy or up to the Denburn were fair blistering in the heat, thick with dust so that the motor-cars went shooming through them like kettles under steam. And serve them right, they'd little care for anybody, the dirt that rode in motors, folk said; and one of them had nearly run over wee Wat Strachan a fortnight before and had skirled to a stop right bang in front of Peesie's Knapp, Wat had yowled like a cat with a jobe under its tail and Chae had gone striding out and taken the motorist man by the shoulder. And *What the hell do you think you're up to?* Chae had asked. And the motorist, he was a fair toff with leggings and a hat cocked over his eyes, he'd said *Keep your damn children off the road in future.* And Chae had said *Keep a civil tongue in your head* and had clouted the motorist

man one in the ear and down he had flumped in the stour and
Mistress Strachan, her that was old Netherhill's daughter, she'd
gone tearing out skirling *Mighty, you brute, you've killed the man!* and
Chae had just laughed and said *Damn the fears!* and off he'd gone.
But Mistress Strachan had helped the toff up to his feet and shook
him and brushed him and apologized for Chae, real civil-like. And
all the thanks she got was that Chae was summonsed for assault at
Stonehaven and fined a pound, and came out of the courthouse
saying there was no justice under capitalism, a revolution would
soon sweep away its corrupted lackeys. And maybe it would, but
faith! there was as little sign of a revolution, said Long Rob of the
Mill, as there was of rain.

*From Sunset Song by Lewis Grassic Gibbon, published by Canongate,
and reprinted by kind permission.*

THE SILVER DARLINGS (1941) *by Neil M. Gunn* DÀIN DO
EIMHIR AGUS DÀIN EILE (Poems to Eimhir and Other Poems)
(1943) *by Somhairle MacGill-Eain (Sorley MacLean)*

All eyes may have been on Europe in the 1940s, but our selection
from this decade comes from the Scottish islands and the sea, and
neither is in any way coloured by the war – not surprising, of course,
given that they were published early in the decade. Works reflecting
the conflict would not begin to appear until later in the 40s,
foremost among them Eric Linklater's satirical novel *Private Angelo*
(1946), about a comic Italian soldier, and folklorist and poet Hamish
Henderson's searing war poems, *Elegies For The Dead In Cyrenaica*
(1948), based on his experiences as a soldier in Europe. For this
collection, Henderson won the Somerset Maugham prize, and for
the first time in his life put a bet – £10 – on the Grand National, at
odds of 66-1. Like his book, he won.

Compared with these two, there is little overtly contemporary about
either of our choices from this decade, but as all who read them on
publication were aware, behind their backward-looking mood was a
very firm grasp on modern reality, and each made its comment on
the current times, albeit subtly.

Neil M. Gunn's *The Silver Darlings*, about the fortunes of the 19th-
century herring industry in his native north-east, is one of the
most popular Scottish novels of all time. It ranks as one of the most
delicate, feeling novels of the century, in Scotland, or anywhere
beyond. Its hero is Finn, a boy whose father died abroad after being
press-ganged by the navy and whose mother has taken up with
another, more successful, man of the sea, who is very different
from her dead husband. Alongside the herring-fishers' story is
that of the indomitable but sensitive Finn who in time becomes
a fisherman like his dad. While it harks back to a previous age,
this novel is full of Gunn's strong socialist sympathies, which had
been strengthened by the poverty he had witnessed in the 1930s.
Stylistically, and to a degree politically, he was influenced by Hugh
MacDiarmid, who in turn praised the younger writer for his "purely
Scottish use of English".

Teacher and poet Sorley MacLean's sonorous *Poems to Eimhir and
Other Poems* was a landmark for Scottish letters. A series of love
poems, it was acclaimed for its linguistic vigour and profundity
when it first was published, but today there is increasing awareness

of just how remarkable MacLean's poetry is. Here, as with Gunn, MacLean finds inspiration in the beauty of his home country. Unlike Gunn, though, MacLean was an out and out modernist. Described by one critic recently as being "as hard as a very hard thing", there's nothing of the cabbage-patch about this Gael, whose work stands shoulder to shoulder with the finest poets of his age.

The 1940s saw a plethora of excellent novels and poetry beyond those mentioned, as if hard times were a mill for the imagination. Some of the other contenders for this period include Naomi Mitchison's fine historical novel *The Bull Calves* (1947), about the 1745 Jacobite Rebellion, Edward Gaitens's acclaimed novel *Dance of the Apprentices* (1948), and Sydney Goodsir Smith's poems, *Under the Eildon Tree* (1948).

Rosemary Goring,
January 2012

THE SILVER DARLINGS *by Neil M. Gunn*

In the grey hours of that morning all Dunster came awake, and men and women buttoned and wrapped themselves firmly and made for the cliffs. The gale was blowing fair in on the beach, the very worst airt for boats any distance along the coast. But by great good luck the herring signs had been off the bay, and the boats had been shot a mile or so out, between the Head and the cliffs to the west. The real danger now lay not in the force of the wind but in the seas the wind would whip up and smash on the beach before they could reach it.

The smaller boats hauled their few nets as swiftly as they could and were soon on their sweeps, coming with the wind at a great pace. The seas were rising rapidly, having the whole weight of an ocean, east by north, behind them. The tide was half in and the worst of the boulders covered. As a boat grounded, the crew leapt into the surf and heaved.

Soon there were sufficient men on shore to give newcomers immediate help. The beach in that morning gloom became a scene of extraordinary activity, with dark bodies rushing and voices crying above the seething waters and the high whining of the gale.

From the cliff-tops the women of the crofts could see the boats coming, and struggled down to the beach, and watched their menfolk advancing and retreating, grasping and hauling, on the edge of the mounting surf as in a wild, infernal dance.

The larger boats, with drifts of twenty nets, lay on a back-rope and found it a dead weight, hard and unyielding under the great pressure of the storm. Many cut clear; others that hung on too long in a desperate effort to save all they could, had to face a beach where high waves were curling over, smashing, and sucking down the shingle in a white roar.

But all boats made the beach, and the bulk of them were hauled clear without any damage done. Indeed, beyond the starting of a few planks and the abandonment of some nets, the Dunster fleet was intact and its fishermen, apart from a minor bruise here and there, unharmed.

As the crowd drifted away from the shore the feeling of delivery was upon them, gratefully in the high-pitched voices of the women, but with the pleasant quiet that follows fighting exultation in the hearts of the men. When a small boy appeared, his father took him by the hand.

Realizing what might have happened had the boats been shot a few miles along the cliffs to the west, many said that Dunster had been fortunate and that news of another kind might well reach them from other fishing stations before the day was done.

The first of that news came with the stage-coach. Mr. Hendry was inmost of the group that gathered round, when Williamson drew his horses to a standstill.

"I made a special point," answered Williamson, "of asking in Helmsdale when I came through. All the boats were accounted for except two – the *Esperance* from the south side and the *Morning Star* from Dunster."

Through the silence Williamson climbed down stiffly.

"No word at all?" demanded the inn-keeper in a sudden loud voice.

"No," said Williamson, pausing to look at the bay where the great combers were smashing on the beach in intermittent booming and a continuous roar. He seemed extraordinarily detached, untouched, like fate.

Mr. Hendry swung abruptly round and went stumping back to his inn at a rapid pace. There he yoked pony to gig, and to a group at the corner shouted, "I'm for Helmsdale." Whipping up the pony, he was off; nor did he stop when man or woman cried to him, but yelled in abrupt response, "I'll be back!"

Mr. Hendry's wealth had been mounting these last years. Helmsdale, his first out-thrust into the greater world, had already assured him of a profit that in the few remaining weeks should handsomely increase. Roddie had become more than a fisherman to Hendry; he had almost become a talisman. Next year, Lybster. The year after, Wick. And then... Not so much money, money, money now in the glitter of silver crowns, as that vast ultimate thing called a fortune. His banker at Wick received him in his parlour.

Now if Roddie and his crew were lost, Mr. Hendry had the superstitious feeling that it would take the heart out of Dunster and in some malign way smash up his designs.

"Hup!" and he used the whip on the sweating horse. Anything to get away from the desperate knowledge, plain to landsman or publican, that no boat could have headed into that sea, that no boat had any place to run for but the harbour or the rocks. Unless, of course, it had beached somewhere along the sandy southward shore or perhaps even have made Portgower – a mocking hope, for in either case word would have been in Helmsdale long before the stage-coach.

From The Silver Darlings by Neil M. Gunn, published by Faber, and reprinted by kind permission.

DÀIN DO EIMHIR AGUS DÀIN EILE (Poems to Eimhir and Other Poems) *by Somhairle MacGill-Eain (Sorley MacLean)*

I

Girl of the red-gold hair,
far from you, love, my pursuit;
girl of the red-gold hair,
far from you my sorrow.

Tonight on the Sound of Raasay my hand is on the helm,
the wind tugs energetically at the sail,
my heart is dumb, aching for your music,
today and tomorrow indifferent to my expectation.

Grey the mist creeping over Dun Caan,
fretful the coarse moorgrass and bog cotton,
a wind from the west touches the surface of the sea,
my hopes are gone, gloom overshadows me.

A white cleft to the bottom of the wave,
the wind skirls round the top of the mast,
but let it blow, I am indifferent
to a battle awakening on a bare sea.

Girl of the red-gold hair,
far from you, love, my pursuit,
girl of the red-gold hair,
very far from you my sorrow.
CW

II
Reason and Love

If our language has said that reason
is identical with love,
it is not speaking the truth.

When my eye lighted on your face
it did not show the reason in love,
I did not ask about that third part.

When I heard your voice it did not make
this division in my flesh;
it did not the first time.

But that came to me without my knowing
and it tore the root of my being,
sweeping me with it in its drift.

With all I had of apprehension
I put up a shadow of fight;
my reason struggled.

From the depths of this old wisdom
I spoke to my love:
you are not worthy of me, nor from me.

    On the inside my love,
    my intellect on the elegant side,
    and the foolish door was broken.

And my intellect said to my love:
duality is not for us;
we mingle in love.

I
A nighean a' chùil ruaidh òir,
fada bhuat, a luaidh, mo thòir;
a nighean a' chùil ruaidh òir,
gur fada bhuatsa mo bhròn.

Mi nochd air linne Ratharsair 's mo làmh air an stiùir,
a' ghaoth gu neo-airstealach a' crathadh an t-siùil,
mo chridhe gu balbh, cràiteach an dèidh do chiùil,
an là an-diugh 's a-màireach coingeis ri mo dhùil.

Ciar an ceò èalaidh air Dùn Cana
frionasach garbh-shliabh is canach,
a' ghaoth an iar air aghaidh mara,
dh'fhalbh mo dhùil is dùiseal tharam.

Am bristeadh geal gu làr an tuinn,
a' ghaoth 'na sgal mu bhàrr a' chroinn,
ach sèideadh sgal, chan eil mo shuim
ri cath a dhùisgeas air muir luim.

A nighean a' chùil ruaidh òir,
fada bhuat, a luaidh, mo thòir;
a nighean a' chùil ruaidh òir,
gur glè fhada bhuat mo bhròn.

II
A Chiall 's a Ghràidh

Ma thubhairt ar cainnt gu bheil a' chiall
co-ionann ris a'ghaol,
chan fhior dhi.

Nuair dhearc mo shùil air t' aodann
cha do nochd e ciall a' ghràidh,
cha do dh'fheòraich mi mun trian ud.

Nuair chuala mi do ghuth cha d' rinn
e 'n roinneadh seo ' nam chrè;
cha d' rinn a' chiad uair.

Ach dhiùchd siud dhomh gun aithne dhomh
is reub e friamh mo chrè,
gam sguabadh leis 'na shiaban.

Leis na bha dhomh de bhreannachadh
gun d' rinn mi faileas strì;
gun d' rinneadh gleac lem chèill.

Bho dhoimhne an t-seann ghliocais seo
's ann labhair mi rim ghaol:
Cha diù leam thu, cha diù bhuam.

Air an taobh a-staigh mo ghaol,
mo thuigse air an taobh ghrinn,
is bhristeadh a' chòmhla bhaoth.

Is thubhairt mo thuigse ri mo ghaol:
Cha dhuinn an dùbailteachd:
tha 'n coimeasgadh sa ghaol.

Translated by Christopher Whyte. Reprinted, by kind permission, from Caoir Gheal / White Leaping Flame: Collected Poems by Sorley MacLean, published by Polygon, an imprint of Birlinn Ltd, in association with Carcanet Press.

1950-1959

YOUNG ADAM (1954) *by Alexander Trocchi*
THE CONE GATHERERS (1955) *by Robert Jenkins*

It would be hard to find two more different novels than Alexander Trocchi's *Young Adam* and Robin Jenkins' *The Cone Gatherers*. The only thing that unites them is the bleakness of their view of the world, and the confidence in their uncompromising voice. In Jenkins' case, this dark perspective was in part attributable to his hard childhood, and his experience of war, as a conscientious objector. Trocchi, a heroin addict who once shot up on live television, was famously described by Hugh MacDiarmid as "cosmopolitan scum". A life spent between fixes, in which he occasionally pimped his wife for money, may explain his pugnacious, anti-establishment outlook.

In order to find a respectable publisher, Trocchi edited the original version of *Young Adam*, removing several sex scenes and an almost comically misogynistic scene near the novel's end. The result is a powerful and disturbing account, by Joe, a most unreliable narrator, of the death of his girlfriend, and his affair with a miserably married woman. Critics consider *Young Adam* the best example of Trocchi's proto-modernism. Whatever label is put upon it, there is no denying the enormous influence this, and others of his works, have had on the collective consciousness of Scotland's modern writers. A less conservative and judgemental country would have embraced this troubled firebrand in his own lifetime, but as is often the way, critical acclaim came too late for the author to enjoy it.

The Cone Gatherers is a much more traditionally composed work, but under its surface it is as angry, and violent, as Trocchi's. Set during World War Two, and using Jenkins' war-time work in the Argyll forests for some of its detail, it's a story of a very personal battle between an embittered gamekeeper and a gentle but simple forester, played out in a seemingly idyllic rural setting. As with much of Jenkins' later work, *The Cone Gatherers* is an exploration of the struggle between good and evil. The elegance and evocativeness of its telling make this modern parable timeless.

Other works published in the fifties give the impression that Scottish writing was beginning to spark off in every direction. In this decade thrillers and comedies such as Ian Fleming's *From Russia with Love* (1957), Alistair MacLean's *The Guns of Navarone* (1957) and

Neil Munro's immortal *Para Handy Tales* (1958) rubbed shoulders with Norman MacCaig's very fine poetry collection *Riding Lights* (1955), James Kennaway's brooding classic, *Tunes of Glory* (1956) and Jessie Kesson's unforgettable autobiographical novel, *The White Bird Passes* (1958). Almost overnight, it seems, Scotland's literary landscape had risen as if from beneath a blanket of ice.

Rosemary Goring,
January 2012

YOUNG ADAM *by Alexander Trocchi*

It had come floating downstream, willowy, like a tangle of weeds. She was beautiful in a pale way – not her face, although that wasn't bad, but the way her body seemed to have given itself to the water, its whole gesture abandoned, the long white legs apart and trailing, sucked downwards slightly at the feet.

As I leaned over the edge of the barge with a boathook I didn't think of her as a dead woman, not even when I looked at the face. She was like some beautiful white water-fungus, a strange shining thing come up from the depths, and her limbs and her flesh had the ripeness and maturity of a large mushroom. But it was the hair more than anything; it stranded away from the head like long grasses. Only it was alive, and because the body was slow, heavy, torpid, it had become a forest of antennae, caressing, feeding on the water, intricately.

It was not until Leslie swore at me for being so handless with the boathook that I drew her alongside. We reached down with our hands. When I felt the chilled flesh under my fingertips I moved more quickly. It was sagging away from us and it slopped softly and obscenely against the bilges. It was touching it that made me realize how bloated it was.

Leslie said: 'For Christ's sake get a bloody grip on it!'

I leaned down until my face was nearly touching the water and with my right hand got hold of one of the ankles. She turned over smoothly then, like the fat underbelly of a fish. Together we pulled her to the surface and, dripping a curtain of river-water, over the gunwale. Her weight settled with a flat, splashing sound on the wooden boards of the deck. Puddles of water formed quickly at the knees and where the chin lay.

We looked at her and then at each other but neither of us said anything. It was obscene, the way death usually is, frightening and obscene at the same time.

'A hundred and thirty at elevenpence a pound': an irrelevant thought...I didn't know how it came to me, and for more than one reason, partly because I knew Leslie would be shocked, I didn't utter it. Later you will see what I mean.

The ambulance didn't arrive until after breakfast. I don't suppose they were in a hurry because I told them she was dead on the telephone. We threw a couple of potato sacks over her so that she wouldn't frighten the kid and then I went over and telephoned and went back and joined Leslie and his wife and the kid at breakfast.

'No egg this morning?' I said.

Ella said no, that she'd forgotten to buy them the previous day when she went to get the stores. But I knew that wasn't true because I'd seen her take them from her basket when she returned. That made me angry, that she didn't take the trouble to remember how she'd examined the shells because she thought she might have broken one of them, and me there in the cabin at the time. It was a kind of insult.

'Salt?' I said, the monosyllable carrying the cynical weight of my disbelief.

'Starin' you in the face,' she said.

It was damp. I had to scrape it from the side of the dish with my knife. Ella ignored the scratching sound and Leslie, his face twitching as it sometimes did, went on reading the paper.

It was only when I had began to eat my bacon that it occurred to me they'd had an egg. I could see the traces on the prongs of their forks. And after I'd gone all the way across the dock to the telephone... Leslie got up noisily, without his second cup of tea. He was embarrassed. Ella had her back to me and I swore at her under my breath. A moment later she too went up on deck, taking the kid with her, and I was left alone to finish my breakfast.

From Young Adam by Alexander Trocchi, published by Oneworld Classics, and reprinted by kind permission.

THE CONE GATHERERS *by Robert Jenkins*

Deer drives can be revealers of personality. A conscript such as Erchie Graham let out at deliberately prolonged intervals snarls and barks and hoots, whose purpose was as much to express his disapproval as to terrify any deer in front of him. Charlie was conscientious, unresentful, and unimaginative. He tried out two or three calls, and decided that the utilitarian 'hoi' was best. He repeated it often. "Hoi, hoi, hoi," he would cry, and then would be silent for the same length of time. That was how he began, but later, when exhaustion and confusion had bewildered him, he often forgot to cry, and had to issue as many as ten 'hois' in a row to make up for his dereliction.

Betty had a generous repertoire. She put both hands to her mouth and yelled Glasgow street cries, such as: "Ripe juicy tomatoes; toys for rags; coal, briquettes." Then she sang, with an exaggeration of her native gallousness, several sentimental ballads of the day. Once when a sharp stick grazed her knee she flyted like a cheated delf wife; her own performance amused her so much she broke into laughter, which she raised gradually in pitch till it was like what she thought a hyena's would be or a crazy person's. That joke over, she sang or rather screamed to the silent senatorial trees some childhood doggerel:

"Auntie Leezie's currant bun!
We sat on the stairs
And we had such fun
Wi' Auntie Leezie's currant bun."

Below her, plunging into his gullies and panting up them, Harry was the intrepid commando, dashing single-handed to the rescue: his cries were threats and challenges to the enemy, and encouragement to his captured comrades.

Neil dourly kept his mouth shut: the noise he made crashing through thickets was enough. Calum, however, was enticed by the beauty of the wood and the mystery of the game; he uttered long melodious calls and little chuckles.

It was Calum who first saw the deer.

The drive was nearly over. Only a hundred or so yards away were the waiting guns. Frightened by the noises approaching them from the rear, and apprehensive of the human silence ahead, the five roe deer were halted, their heads high in nervous alertness. When Calum saw them, his cry was of delight and friendship, and then of terrified warning as the dogs too, and Duror, caught sight of them and rushed in pursuit. Silently, with marvellous grace and agility over such rough ground, the deer flew for the doom ahead. Their white behinds were like moving glints of sunlight; without them their tawny hides might not have been seen in the autumnal wood.

Calum no longer was one of the beaters; he too was a deer hunted by remorseless men. Moaning and gasping, he fled after them, with no hope of saving them from slaughter but with the impulse to share it with them. He could not, however, be so swift or sure of foot. He fell and rose again; he avoided one tree only to collide with another close to it; and all the time he felt, as the deer must have, the indifference of all nature; of the trees, of tall withered stalks of willowherb, of the patches of blue sky, of bushes, of piles of cut scrubwood, of birds lurking in branches, and of the sunlight: presences which might have been expected to help or at least sympathise.

From *The Cone Gatherers* by Robin Jenkins, *published by Canongate, and reprinted by kind permission.*

THE PRIME OF MISS JEAN BRODIE (1961) *by Muriel Spark*
A HISTORY OF THE SCOTTISH PEOPLE 1560-1830 (1969)
by T. C. Smout

Some books stand out like lighthouses. Across the century Scottish
writers produced works of such quality and originality they have
indelibly altered the literary landscape. Few, however, have made
such a popular and critical impact at home and internationally
as Muriel Spark's *The Prime of Miss Jean Brodie*, which has some
claim to being the most perfect Scottish novel ever written. With
the war safely in the rear mirror, Spark was able to evoke, in the
seemingly douce setting of an Edinburgh girls' school, the sinister
but seductive shadow of fascism. In her spirited school-teacher
Jean Brodie, who wielded inordinate power over her pupils, Spark
created a literary character whose intrepid, intolerant spirit was the
essence of middle-class Scotland. In her own way, however, she was
a rebel who sowed trouble all around, and showed readers just how
dangerous a charismatic personality with unsound judgement
can be.

Another towering achievement, and the only work of non-fiction
selected for Scotland's Bookshelf, is Professor T. C. Smout's *A
History of the Scottish People 1560-1830*. Until relatively recently,
Scottish history has often been the poor cousin of English
and world history, taught fleetingly, or not at all in schools and
universities. Smout was one of the foremost historians of his day to
shed new light on Scotland's past, focusing on social and economic
events rather than the purely political. That in itself is not enough,
of course, to make for great written history. What makes *A History
of the Scottish People* stand out is Smout's originality of thought, and
winning, compelling style. This scholarly yet brave work describes
and explains the country's evolution, through arguably its most
formative years, yet it reads less like history than like a story, where
one can't help but turn the next page, and the next. Such was its
success on publication that one southern critic commented that
even the English should read it. Forty years on it remains in print,
and can still be found in homes where previously there had been no
other history books.

This was, though, a decade in which literature of all kinds
flourished. Among the stiff competition for a place on the
bookshelf were novels such as Alan Sharp's *A Green Tree in Gedde*
(1965), which had the distinction of being banned from Edinburgh's

libraries for including incestuous characters, Archie Hind's soul-searching *The Dear Green Place* (1966), and Iain Crichton Smith's *Consider the Lilies* (1968, written in a fortnight), as well as children's novelist Kathleen Fidler's historical novel *The Desperate Journey* (1964, one of 12 books she published this decade) and John Prebble's colourful history, *Culloden* (1961).

Rosemary Goring,
January 2012

THE PRIME OF MISS JEAN BRODIE *by Muriel Spark*

Joyce Emily said, 'There's a teacher coming out,' and nodded towards the gates.

Two of the Andrews wheeled their bicycles out on to the road and departed. The other three boys remained defiantly, but looking the other way as if they might have stopped to admire the clouds on the Pentland Hills. The girls crowded round each other as if in discussion. 'Good afternoon,' said Miss Brodie when she approached the group. 'I haven't seen you for some days. I think we won't detain these young men and their bicycles. Good afternoon, boys.' The famous set moved off with her, and Joyce, the new delinquent, followed. 'I think I haven't met this new girl,' said Miss Brodie, looking closely at Joyce. And when they were introduced she said: 'Well, we must be on our way, my dear.'

Sandy looked back as Joyce Emily walked, and then skipped, leggy and uncontrolled for her age, in the opposite direction, and the Brodie set was left to their secret life as it had been six years ago in their childhood.

'I am putting old heads on your young shoulders,' Miss Brodie had told them at that time, 'and all my pupils are the crème de la crème.'

Sandy looked with her little screwed-up eyes at Monica's very red nose and remembered this saying as she followed the set in the wake of Miss Brodie.

'I should like you girls to come to supper tomorrow night,' Miss Brodie said. 'Make sure you are free.'

'The Dramatic Society...' murmured Jenny.

'Send an excuse,' said Miss Brodie. 'I have to consult you about a new plot which is afoot to force me to resign. Needless to say, I shall not resign.' She spoke calmly as she always did in spite of her forceful words.

Miss Brodie never discussed her affairs with the other members of the staff, but only with those former pupils whom she had trained up in her confidence. There had been previous plots to remove her from Blaine, which had been foiled.

'It has been suggested again that I should apply for a post at one of the progressive schools, where my methods would be more suited to the system than they are at Blaine. But I shall not apply for a post at a crank school. I shall remain at this education factory.

There needs must be a leaven in the lump. G ive me a girl at an impressionable age, and she is mine for life.'

The Brodie set smiled in understanding of various kinds.

Miss Brodie forced her brown eyes to flash as a meaningful accompaniment to her quiet voice. She looked a mighty woman with her dark Roman profile in the sun. The Brodie set did not for a moment doubt that she would prevail. As soon expect Julius Caesar to apply for a job at a crank school as Miss Brodie. She would never resign. If the authorities wanted to get rid of her she would have to be assassinated.

'Who are the gang, this time?' said Rose, who was famous for sex-appeal.

'We shall discuss tomorrow night the persons who oppose me,' said Miss Brodie. 'But rest assured they shall not succeed.'

'No,' said everyone. 'No, of course they won't.'

'Not while I am in my prime,' she said. 'These years are still the years of my prime. It is important to recognize the years of one's prime, always remember that. Here is my tram-car. I dare say I'll not get a seat. This is nineteen-thirty-six. The age of chivalry is past.'

From The Prime of Miss Jean Brodie by Muriel Spark, published by Jonathan Cape. Reprinted by kind permission of The Random House Group Limited

A HISTORY OF THE SCOTTISH PEOPLE 1560-1830
by T. C. Smout

Edinburgh attracted five times as many noblemen and gentry as Glasgow even in 1773, and the proportion would be much larger fifty years later when the New Town in the capital was completed. There were in fact no nobles living in Glasgow (several dukes and earls had property in Edinburgh) and many of the 'gentry' living there could probably be more aptly described as merchants with estates. Again, the occupation of 'room-setter' in Edinburgh (usually carried on by a widow or maiden lady) had no real counterpart in Glasgow: it also reflected the capital's prestige as a social centre in which to spend the season, as a tourist centre, and as a centre for education with a large student population needing lodgings. Shipmasters lived at Leith (in the area covered by the Edinburgh directory) but not in the environs of Glasgow at that date, when the Clyde was still only fifteen inches deep at low water: they lived down the water at Port Glasgow and Greenock, and the only nautical men at Glasgow were boatmen who took travellers and goods in barges along or across the Clyde. Against these contrasts, it is interesting that sellers of food and drink were equally numerous in both cities: most of them were sellers of drink – Hugo Arnot calculated in 1779 that there were somewhere between 1600 and 2000 ale sellers in Edinburgh, and they were at least as numerous in the west. One of the problems of analysing the Glasgow Directory was deciding in which pigeon hole to put some of the sellers of drink, as it was obviously a part-time occupation of many tradesmen: where is one to place Walter McAdam, vinter and horse setter, or John Elder, cordiner and spirit dealer? Even barbers in Glasgow sometimes combined cutting hair and letting blood with selling restorative alcohol.

More significant differences were revealed in the remaining categories. Glasgow had an appreciable professional class – with a university and several noted schools, and with the need for locally-based lawyers and notaries to oil the wheels of trade, but it was less than half as important as that of Edinburgh in proportion to the size of the two cities. Similarly, Edinburgh had a significant business class, composed partly of traditional merchants who imported and exported through Leith and partly of newer men such as the bankers and the masters of sugar houses or printing works: she had a still larger class of tradesmen and artisans who ministered in innumerable ways to the needs of middle-class residents and visiting gentry. But in Glasgow the business class was more than twice as large, and the artisan class was half as large again even though only the most 'middle-class' artisans would have found an entry in such a directory. The expression 'manufacturer', which occurs repeatedly in the Glasgow directory, is not known at all in the Edinburgh one. It is interesting that in Edinburgh nearly one in three of all the entrants in the directory was a professional man, and one in eight a 'businessman': in Glasgow one in eight was a professional man, and one in three a businessman – exactly the reverse proportions if the source is an accurate guide.

The greatness of Glasgow was built upon the entrepreneurial skill of her businessmen, whether merchants or manufacturers. Enterprise and resilience had been their noted attributes over a long period. Even in the seventeenth century, when Scottish merchants generally had a bad reputation of unadventurousness, those of Glasgow were pressing forward horizons to the West Indies and America when this meant smuggling ships and goods past the English administrators of the Navigation Acts; they were also establishing sugar refineries, cloth manufactories, soapworks, distilleries and so on, indicative of a precocious willingness to adventure with novel industrial techniques. In the eighteenth century, especially after 1740 when economic expansion was much more rapid, observers noted again and again the initiative of the Glasgow man, his 'spirit of industry' and catholic interest in novelty.

From A History of the Scottish People 1560-1830 by T. C. Smout, published by Harper Collins.

1970-1979

GREENVOE (1972) *by George Mackay Brown*
DOCHERTY (1975) *by William McIlvanney*

Like summer nights in June, by the 1970s the roster of good Scottish books is growing longer and longer. Those we chose between read like a roll-call of some of the finest writers of our times, whose names are recognised across the world. There's the likes of Elspeth Davie's gently devastating short stories, *The High Tide Talker* (1976) or Alan Spence's *Its Colours They Are Fine* (1977), Joan Lingard's groundbreaking political children's novel *Across the Barricades* (1972), and former convict Jimmy Boyle's sobering and soul-baring autobiography, *A Sense of Freedom* (1977). That's before mentioning poetry such as Tom Leonard's acclaimed collection *Glasgow Poems* (1976), Edwin Morgan's experimental *From Glasgow to Saturn* (1973) and Douglas Dunn's tender *Love or Nothing* (1974). Where should one start?

There was probably a touch of sentimentality in our choice of George Mackay Brown's first novel, *Greenvoe*, for this decade, as there certainly is in the novel itself. Yet no selection of the best books of the century would be complete without including the Orcadian bard, and while one could argue that this is not his finest work, it is nevertheless a gem of a book, bringing alive a fictional Orkney island and the threat of extinction faced by the village of Greenvoe when a high-tech and highly secret military project makes the village its base. Though short on plot, this closely framed story of local characters and outside interests draws for its power on Mackay Brown's poetic eye, and his feeling for the heart and soul of his native land. And it is unforgettable. Even the simplest domestic sentence is telling: "The mince pot and the potato pot and the cabbage pot bubbled on the moons of the stove."

Where Mackay Brown set his novel in the 1960s, William McIlvanney's third novel, *Docherty*, drew on the first half of the 20th century for its backdrop, as he depicts some of the political, social and emotional struggles of the working-classes, in the guise of miner Tam, and his eagle-eyed son Conn. Himself the son of a miner, McIlvanney knew what he was talking about as he threw into relief the hardships and intellectual challenges his hero and son face. "He's a wee man but he makes a big shadda," he writes of the doughty miner, who has to claw his and his family's way through the great depression.

Docherty was the first of McIlvanney's novels to become truly influential. It won him the Whitbread Novel Award, but more importantly it sealed his reputation as one of the finest and most uncompromising writers of his generation. With his next novel, *Laidlaw*, whose hero was a thoughtful, troublesome detective, some readers mistakenly believed he had moved into crime. In fact, with this complex, dark emotional thriller, he used all the skills and imagination he had brought to *Docherty* to kickstart what has since become the most popular Scottish literary genre. But *Laidlaw*, like *Docherty*, is a one-off, and defies any label. Beyond the pleasures of the novel itself, it represents an important new voice and style in Scottish writing which many have since tried to emulate. As the years have shown, however, McIlvanney is inimitable.

Rosemary Goring,
January 2012

GREENVOE *by George Mackay Brown*

In the endless bestiary of the weather the unicorns of cloud are littered far west in the Atlantic; the sun their sire, the sea their dame. Swiftly they hatch and flourish. They travel eastwards, a grey silent stampeding herd. Their shining hooves beat over the Orkneys and on out into the North Sea. Sometimes it takes days for that migration to pass. But many are torn on the crags and hills, and spill their precious ichor on the farm-lands. Crofters wake to cornfields and pastures extravagantly jewelled.

Bert Kerston was awakened by a steady tap on the ben window. He rose at once and pulled on his trousers. He left the warm snoring hulk at his side. He groped his way through a scatter of sweetly breathing cribs and cradles. He took a black oilskin from the hook on the wall and put it on. His thigh-boots stood in the corner, long collapsed tubes; he eased his legs into them.

Bert Kerston boiled the kettle on the primus stove and made himself a pot of tea. The rain lashed against the window. He spread a barley scone first with butter and then with rhubarb jam. The tea in the pint mug was too hot; he slopped some over into a saucer. Tom turned over in his bed and threw his arm over Ernie and sighed once and breathed regularly and slowly again. Bert Kerston sucked the last drops of tea out of his moustache. He passed out into the pouring morning.

Samuel Whaness in his oilskin passed, going down to the *Siloam*. The two fishermen met outside Timmy Folster's burnt window. 'To think,' said Bert Kerston to Samuel Whaness, 'that we have to slave our guts out in every kind of weather, and pay national insurance, to keep bloody scum like that! I could hardly get a wink of sleep for him all night.'

Samuel Whaness, his mouth holy from praise and scripture, passed on without a word down to his boat.

Bert Kerston stood against the latrine wall and added his bladder trickle to the steaming surging pier.

Samuel Whaness's engine started up.

The Skarf woke with a dry throat. (How many pints had Ivan Westray given him in Scorradale's last night? Six, maybe seven.) He rose in his shirt and drawers and poured himself a cup of water from the jug and went back to bed. Well, it wasn't weather to fish, that was one thing sure. A name emerged from his ruck of half-awakened perceptions: Thorvald Harvest-Happy. About this man nothing was known. Thorvald Harvest-Happy got one sentence in the saga. But there was an indwelling image; it stepped out of the name and drew other images about itself: a glebe, a great barn, a host of labourers, seedtime and harvest, snow and sun, a sprinkling with water, a kiss, a death-sweat. And a rhythm smote upon the host of images, pulsed through them, and gave them an ordering in time, so that they were gathered into a single dance.

The Skarf flung the blankets from him and dragged on trousers and jersey. He sat down between his tea-boxes of books. He took up his ball-point and opened the old cash-book on his desk.

It is going to be a long session today, Mrs McKee thought, putting the lid back on the marmalade. Already the black shapes were astir at the edge of her consciousness, there were whispers, scurries, consultations. Normally the trial began in the early afternoon, once the last soup plate was back on the dresser rack and Simon had gone into his study. Well, there was nothing else for it; if she was summoned she was summoned, she would have to hear them out, that was all. She had so much wanted that morning to visit Mr Budge the old sailor, who was quite ill, she had heard him coughing terribly all night. He swore a great deal, but that was just the way of sailors, he was a very nice old man for all that, and his sister was just delightful, the way she spoke to the hens and everything.

From Greenvoe by George Mackay Brown, published by Polygon, an imprint of Birlinn Ltd, and reprinted by kind permission.

DOCHERTY *by William McIlvanney*

Danny's arrival meant that he and Mick would soon be going for the train and everybody came together frenetically in last attempts to say what they had been wanting to say and to touch and to extract a final essence from the occasion. In the scrum of affection the form of what was happening was lost, and then suddenly Mick and Danny were among the men and moving towards the door. Jean was lying back on her pillow, lips compressed and wet with her own tears, the sensation of Mick's embrace still warm on her cheek. Kathleen was standing herself, just crying. Tam was gently easing Jenny out of Mick's arms and Mary Hawkins was being prised way from Danny. Then the men receded like a tide and left the women stranded in an empty room.

The group collected more men at the corner. By the time they reached the station, they were a small battalion. On the platform they stamped and jostled, waiting for the train that would take Mick and Danny on the first stage of their journey to their camp on the east coast. Their breaths fluttered around them, a cluster of small pennants. Their voices were raucous, trying to match the size of the situation. There was a lot of determined laughter. People laid hands on Mick and Danny till they bruised.

The train just saved the whole thing from hysteria. Seats were found and the men who had been carrying the kitbags left them while everybody piled out again and Mick and Danny stood at the window. With about a minute to go Kathleen, pregnant as she was, came running along the platform. They had forgotten the fags which were to be shared between them as a parting gift. Also, Mick's grandmother had been meaning to give them a clothes-brush each as an extra item of kit.

'We've goat wan,' Mick said.

But they had to take them.

'No somethin' else,' Danny said, laughing. 'Christ, ma mither wantit me tae take the chist o' drawers. But it widny fit intae ma kitbag.'

Those were the famous last words of their departure. The train was moving. In spite of all the careful preparation that had gone into the evening, the heart of it was in that suddenness, the clank of the wheel-rods, the chuff and lurch of the train, the wrench of distance. The rest of it had only been a ceremony for discovering that surprise, for savouring it by contrast. The real farewell was in those slightly shocked expressions, the words deflected by the wind, the gestures that fell into the distance.

From Docherty by William McIlvanney, © William McIlvanney 1975, reproduced by permission of the publisher Hodder and Stoughton Limited.

THE WASP FACTORY (1984) *by Iain Banks*
A QUESTION OF LOYALTIES (1989) *by Allan Massie*

Looking back, it feels as if someone threw petrol on the fire, such is the blaze of good writing that lit up the literary scene in this decade. Perhaps the spark was the political frustration that followed the country's failed bid for devolution in 1979. Or perhaps that had nothing to do with it. All that can be said with confidence is that in these years Scotland saw the most concentrated and vigorous upsurge of literary talent ever witnessed in its history, a phenomenon that carried on well into the following decade, and showed no sign of abating in the first ten years of the new millennium.

It was the decade when such notable figures as Alasdair Gray, Janice Galloway and James Kelman first began to make a name for themselves, along with those such as Carl MacDougall, Christopher Rush and Frederic Lindsay. It was also the era in which Iain Banks burst onto the scene. His extraordinary first novel is one of the choices for this decade. When it was published, *The Wasp Factory* brought Banks critical acclaim but also, from some quarters, severe condemnation. Rarely, if ever, in the history of Scottish literature had such a violent, disturbing novel seen the light of day. Written from the perspective of teenage psychopath Frank as he recalls his childhood, and the traumas he and his family had suffered, it matter of factly, and at times almost drolly described the killings of animals, children, and of course wasps, that Frank had carried out in his short life. Some readers were repelled, rather than impressed. The Irish Times called it "a work of unparalleled depravity" and it certainly takes a strong stomach to read it. And yet it has become one of the iconic novels of its times, and its influence on later generations of novelists has been profound.

The Wasp Factory can be seen as a brilliantly savage response to the grim (and worsening) political and social climate in which Banks wrote it, when Margaret Thatcher's Conservative government was in full cry, and Scotland suffering under its often draconian policies. It is also, more directly, about the ties between a father and his children.

Allan Massie's *A Question of Loyalties* is also about a father and son, as explored in the setting of post-war France, when a young man searches for the truth about his father, and how he behaved during the occupation: was he a patriot, as he'd always thought, or in fact a treacherous collaborator? And if so, what does this mean for their relationship? A subtle, atmospheric and deeply moving account of what war can do to individuals, and how their actions should be viewed by those who follow after them, *A Question of Loyalties* is arguably Massie's finest work to date and takes its place alongside the best historical novels this country has produced.

Rosemary Goring,
January 2012

THE WASP FACTORY *by Iain Banks*

I had decided I would try to murder Esmerelda before she and her parents even arrived for their holiday. Eric was away on a school cruise, so there would only be me and her. It would be risky, so soon after Paul's death, but I had to do something to even up the balance. I could feel it in my guts, in my bones; I *had* to. It was like an itch, something I had no way of resisting, like when I walk along a pavement in Porteneil and I accidentally scuff one heel on a paving stone. I *have* to scuff the other foot as well, with as near as possible the same weight, to feel good again. The same if I brush one arm against a wall or a lamp-post; I must brush the other one as well, soon, or at the very least scratch it with the other hand. In a whole range of ways like that I try to keep balanced, though I have no idea why. It is simply something that must be done; and, in the same way, I had to get rid of *some* woman, tip the scales back in the other direction.

I had taken to making kites that year. It was 1973, I suppose. I used many things to make them: cane and dowling and metal coathangers and aluminium tent-poles, and paper and plastic sheeting and dustbin bags and sheets and string and nylon rope and twine and all sorts of little straps and buckles and bits of cord and elastic bands and strips of wire and pins and screws and nails and pieces cannibalised from model yachts and various toys. I made a hand winch with a double handle and a ratchet and room for half a kilometre of twine on the drum; I made different types of tails for the kites that needed them, and dozens of kites large and small, some stunters. I kept them in the shed and eventually had to put the bikes outside under a tarpaulin when the collection got too large.

That summer I took Esmerelda kiting quite a lot. I let her play with a small, single-string kite while I used a stunter. I would send it swooping over and under hers, or dive it down to the sands while I stood on a dune cliff, pulling the kite down to nick tall towers of sand I'd built, then pulling up again, the kite trailing a spray of sand through the air from the collapsing tower. Although it took a while and I crashed a couple of times, once I even knocked a dam down with a kite. I swooped it so that on each pass it caught the top of the dam wall with one corner, gradually producing a nick in the sand barrier which the water was able to flow through, quickly going on to overwhelm the whole dam and the sand-house village beneath.

Then one day I was standing there on a dune top, straining against the pull of the wind in the kite, gripping and hauling and sensing and adjusting and twisting, when one of those twists became like a strangle around Esmerelda's neck, and the idea was there. Use the kites.

I thought about it calmly, still standing there as though nothing had passed through my mind but the continual computation guiding the kite, and I thought it seemed reasonable. As I thought about it, the notion took its own shape, blossoming, as it were, and escalating into what I finally conceived as my cousin's nemesis. I grinned then, I recall, and brought the stunter down fast and acute across the weeds and the water, the sand and the surf, scudding it in across the wind to jerk and zoom just before it hit the girl herself where she sat on the dune top holding and spasmodically jerking the string she held in her hand, connected to the sky. She turned, smiled and shrieked then, squinting in the summer light. I laughed too, controlling the thing in the skies above and the thing in the brain beneath, equally well.

From The Wasp Factory by Iain Banks, published by Little, Brown, and reprinted by kind permission.

A QUESTION OF LOYALTIES *by Allan Massie*

ENTR'ACTE

1951-59

Over the next few years it was only from Jeanne-Marie that I heard. She wrote to me every two to three months, though I rarely replied, and then briefly. I had conceived a loathing of France and the French, and there were times when this seemed even to extend to my dear and delightful cousin. Those were bad years for me, and I don't want to write about them. Fortunately they are not part of the story which I am trying to tell, for there is little in the memory of that period of my life which does not make my flesh crawl with shame and disgust. There was indeed too much flesh in it. I had, through my grandfather's influence, found myself a job in a merchant bank – it would be more exact to say that the job was provided for me. I worked hard because industry deadens feeling, and I was successful. None of my colleagues can have felt any warmth for me, and I was satisfied with this.

Everyone I slept with was Freddie, and I abused them. Looking back, I think I was a bit mad in my twenties.

I had one contact with France. Twice a year I wrote to my grandmother, a formal, cold letter in which I assured her I was well and enquired after her health. I was perversely pleased to perform this dead duty. I told her how much money I was making. It was a sort of mocking triumph.

Jeanne-Marie wrote to me that Freddie was married, then that she was going to have a baby, then that she had lost the child, and sunk into depression. I told myself she wasn't even a memory, though scarcely a night passed that I didn't long for her. Jeanne-Marie informed me that Freddie had been committed to a clinic, that she had run away, taken a car, crashed it and killed herself. 'Whenever we met in these last months, she used to talk of you, Etienne. With a faraway look in her eyes. It was terrible what was done.'

So we were both victims. Very well. I picked up a slut in a coffee-bar and took her to Brighton for the weekend. I doubt if it was what she had hoped for. Anyway, there was a bit of bother, we were asked to leave the hotel, and only my full wallet prevented it from becoming a police matter. When we parted, she told me I should see a doctor. I think that was brave of her, and kind, in the circumstances. Needless to say, I didn't follow her advice; not then. Psychoanalysis came later; without success.

The next death was my grandmother's. I was in New York at the time, and so there was no question of my attending the funeral. Probably I wouldn't have gone anyway. But I was, of course, her principal heir. It was necessary to visit Provence. I travelled south in the first days of December.

The business with lawyers was transacted as briskly as is possible with French country notaries. My own experience had made me sharp in such affairs (as in those which, for want of a better term, may be called 'of the heart'). I was aware that they looked on me with some curiosity, but I answered few of their questions and no direct ones. It was impossible to say what I would do with my inheritance.

My visit to the house was brief. Its air of desolation was more intense than I remembered and anyway the *mistral* was blowing. Marthe had gone – had Jeanne-Marie told me of that? – and a slatternly domestic was acting as caretaker. I confirmed her in her post and told her that I would arrange for the lawyer to continue to pay her wages. Why now? Someone had to live there.

My grandmother had gone out of life very neatly. There was only a tiny void where she had been. Her smell still lingered in her bedroom, and the velvet that covered the *prie-Dieu* was worn to shreds.

I unlocked the Bluebeard's Chamber that had been my father's study. The room was cold and damp, but I sat there behind his desk, and smoked a cigar. It was later that I had his papers collected and sent to me in London.

I stayed in the hotel in the town and ate little and badly. After my meal I took a turn along the street but, soon defeated by the morose wind and rain, returned to the hotel bar and settled myself with a cigar and the inevitable *pastis* of the South, which, without meaning to, I had felt myself compelled to order. There was a group of four men playing cards and drinking *pastis* like myself, while half a dozen young men disported themselves around a billiard table.

One of them broke away and lounged across the room in my direction. He swung out a chair from the table and sat astride it, his forearms resting on its back. He looked at me without removing the cigarette which dangled from the corner of his mouth.

'I've been wondering when you would show up,' he said. 'You don't remember me?'

I didn't like the mockery in his eyes and told him that I had no recollection of him at all. But I did of course; it was Marthe's son Yves. He had been angry before; now my first impression was that he had come to terms with himself. Yet there was something repellent in his air of a lounging beast, the suggestion which emanated from him, that always, given the chance or the opportunity, he would do the dirt on life. So it amused me to force him to tell me who he was, to admit to having made less impression than he was accustomed to leave.

From A Question of Loyalties by Allan Massie, published by Canongate, and reprinted by kind permission.

SWING HAMMER SWING! (1992) *by Jeff Torrington*
TRAINSPOTTING (1993) *by Irvine Welsh*

Irvine Welsh's novel *Trainspotting* hit the literary scene like a runaway express. Almost from the day it was published it became a word of mouth success, and has since gone on to become one of the most famous and influential Scottish novels of the modern age. In 1993, though, this story of four gallus, shamelessly feral young men from Leith, renowned at the time as the heroin capital of Europe, seemed to come out of nowhere. Its heroes, if they can be called that – Renton, Sick Boy, Begbie and Spud – indulge in drink and drugs the way other folk breathe and eat. Written in various voices, in a high-octane series of interior monologues, the novel's raw energy, its insight into the unsettling underbelly of feckless urban life and above all its flinty humour set it on a pedestal all its own. Though it had its precursors, Alexander Trocchi high among them (Welsh describes him as "the Scottish George Best of the literary world"), *Trainspotting* was unique. It also tapped into the mood of the times, when a loathing of convention and the humdrum were never more in fashion, and self-destruction via various addictions was the order of the day.

If *Trainspotting* finally put Edinburgh on the page of the atlas marked 'gritty urban realism', Jeff Torrington's *Swing Hammer Swing!* opened a window onto a vista of Glasgow history from the 1960s that plucked at the heart strings. A former car production-line worker, and well into his fifties when this, his first novel was published, Torrington used humour to make his story come alive, and to emphasise his very political, and personal, points. The only mallet found in this work is that used to bring down a Gorbals tenement. Tam Clay, his hero, is about to become a father, as well as homeless, in the week it takes for him to tell his story. What follows is a sort of modern monologue, in which the vibrancy of Torrington's use of west-coast Scots fizzes with life and attitude. *Trainspotting* was a record of the present, and *Swing Hammer Swing!* a testament to times now past, but each is a highly individual tribute to Scottish experience that has now been enshrined in amber.

The 1990s saw a tsunami of Scottish writing, of a quality and quantity hitherto unknown. There are too many contenders for this decade to list, but among the novels the judges had to wrangle over were Alan Warner's unforgettable debut *Morvern Callar*

(1995), Andrew Greig's bleakly romantic *Electric Brae* (1992), Frank Kuppner's moving, witty and unclassifiable *Something Very Like Murder* (1994), Agnes Owens's wry *For the Love of Willie* (1998), Ronald Frame's tragic novel of youthful infatuation, *The Lantern Bearers* (1999), Laura Hird's darkly comic novel of a troubled Edinburgh family, *Born Free* (1999), and Candia McWilliam's fictional exploration of middle-class confusion in *Debatable Land* (1994). Then there were collections of poetry from Carol Ann Duffy (*The World's Wife*, 1999) and Kathleen Jamie (*Jizzen*, 1999), to name only two.

Rosemary Goring,
January 2012

SWING HAMMER SWING! *by Jeff Torrington*

'Are you still scribbling away then, Tommy?'

He asked this as if he was enquiring about some disease which might not yet've run its course. My shrug seemed to signal that a cure'd been effected. 'Ach, aye,' he said, 'writing books is fine for them that's nothing more to do with their time.' With a surprising expertise for one who claimed to be a teetotaller he flipped over the last of his drink then placed the drained glass on the ledge of the tiled fireplace. 'Anyway,' he announced, indicating the wally dug on the mantlepiece – a cretinous-looking beast with a sawn-off face – 'your books'll soon be as auld-fashioned as one of these things. D'you not think so yourself? This time, next century, they'll be playing bingo in your libraries. Mark my words.'

Aye, nuclear bingo: clickety-click the planet is sick.

I undid another shirt button.

'You've not'd much luck with the book I'm hearing.'

That had to be the understatement of the year. The novel, written by me during my self-allocated sabbatical, had been rejected four times thus far. I've no doubt that behind my back the family were having a good snigger. Rhona of course had been the loyal exception though I admit that her piteous expressions when the thing limped home battered and bloodied by franking stamps, were harder to bear than her sister's outright sarcasm: 'Has your boomerang got back yet, Patton?' she'd enquire, while her husband Jack would give the knife in my back an extra twist by asking if I'd managed to sell any of my daubs? Which meant that he presumed I'd jacked in the railways to pursue a painting career. Maybe I should have. The manuscript had begun to show the bruises from its days, weeks, and months buried in the 'slush piles' of various publishing firms. After it'd been returned for the third time it had scorch marks on several of its pages, as if someone had been trying to thrust the thing into the furnace. Last time out it returned stained by beetroot juice and ketchup which suggested the reader had considered eating it then chickened. So far on this its latest journey southwards, it'd produced an acknowledgement of receipt then thereafter entered into the agonising silent phase which apparently the current Apollo spaceship will encounter when, going behind the moon, it will temporarily sever contact with its Control in Houston.

Actual criticism of the novel by its rejectors was very thin on the ground, although the consensus of opinion seemed to indicate that its main weakness lay in its apparent 'lack of plot'. You can bet your granny's boots and braces it lacks plot. Plots are for graveyards. I'd rather drag my eyeballs along barbed wire than read a plotty novel. You can almost see the authors of such contrived claptrap winding up their childish prose toys, before sending them whirring across their fatuous pages in search of 'adventures'. See how perkily they strut and stride; observe the zany intermingling patterns they make with their inky bootees; listen, and you'll hear their valorous hearts grinding within their heroic breasts.

From Swing Hammer Swing! by Jeff Torrington, published by Minerva. Reprinted by kind permission of The Random House Group Limited.

TRAINSPOTTING *by Irvine Welsh*

The Skag Boys, Jean-Claude Van Damme and Mother Superior

The sweat wis lashing oafay Sick Boy; he wis trembling. Ah wis jist sitting thair, focusing oan the telly, tryin no tae notice the cunt. He wis bringing me doon. Ah tried tae keep ma attention oan the Jean-Claude Van Damme video.

As happens in such movies, they started oaf wi an obligatory dramatic opening. Then the next phase ay the picture involved building up the tension through introducing the dastardly villain and sticking the weak plot thegither. Any minute now though, auld Jean-Claude's ready tae git doon tae some serious swedgin.

— Rents. Ah've goat tae see Mother Superior, Sick Boy gasped, shaking his heid.

— Aw, ah sais. Ah wanted the radge tae jist fuck off ootay ma visage, tae go oan his ain, n jist leave us wi Jean-Claude. Oan the other hand, ah'd be gitting sick tae before long, and if that cunt went n scored, he'd haud oot oan us. They call um Sick Boy, no because he's eywis sick wi junk withdrawal, but because he's just one sick cunt.

— Let's fuckin go, he snapped desperately.

— Haud oan a second. Ah wanted tae see Jean-Claude smash up this arrogant fucker. If we went now, ah wouldnae git tae watch it. Ah'd be too fucked by the time we goat back, and in any case it wid probably be a few days later. That meant ah'd git hit fir fuckin back charges fi the shoap oan a video ah hudnae even goat a deek at.

— Ah've goat tae fuckin move man! he shouts, standing up. He moves ower tae the windae and rests against it, breathing heavily, looking like a hunted animal. There's nothing in his eyes but need.

Ah switched the box oaf at the handset. — Fuckin waste. That's aw it is, a fuckin waste, ah snarled at the cunt, the fuckin irritating bastard.

He flings back his heid n raises his eyes tae the ceiling. — Ah'll gie ye the money tae git it back oot. Is that aw yir sae fuckin moosey-faced aboot? Fifty measley fuckin pence ootay Ritz!

This cunt has a wey ay makin ye feel a real petty, trivial bastard.

— That's no the fuckin point, ah sais, but withoot conviction.

— Aye. The point is ah'm really fuckin sufferin here, n ma so-called mate's draggin his feet deliberately, lovin every fuckin minute ay it! His eyes seem the size ay fitba's n look hostile, yet pleadin at the same time; poignant testimonies tae ma supposed betrayal. If ah ever live long enough tae huv a bairn, ah hope it never looks at us like Sick Boy does. The cunt is irresistible oan this form.

— Ah wisnae… ah protested.

— Fling yir fuckin jaykit oan well!

At the Fit ay the Walk thir wir nay taxis. They only congregated here when ye didnae need them. Supposed tae be August, but ah'm fuckin freezing ma baws oaf here. Ah'm no sick yet, but it's in the fuckin post, that's fir sure.

— Supposed tae be a rank. Supposed tae be a fuckin taxi rank. Nivir fuckin git one in the summer. Up cruising fat, rich festival cunts too fuckin lazy tae walk a hundred fuckin yards fae one poxy church hall tae another fir thir fuckin show. Taxi drivers. Money-grabbin bastards… Sick Boy muttered deliriously and breathlessly tae hissel, eyes bulging and sinews in his neck straining as his heid craned up Leith Walk.

At last one came. There were a group ay young guys in shell-suits n bomber jaykits whae'd been standin thair longer than us. Ah doubt if Sick Boy even saw them. He charged straight oot intae the middle ay the Walk screaming:— TAXI!

— Hi! Whit's the fuckin score? One guy in a black, purple and aqua shell-suit wi a flat-top asks.

— Git tae fuck. We wir here first, Sick Boy sais, opening the taxi door. — Thir's another yin comin. He gestured up the Walk at an advancing black cab.

— Lucky fir youse. Smart cunts.

— Fuck off, ya plukey-faced wee hing oot. Git a fuckin ride! Sick Boy snarled as we piled intae the taxi.

— Tollcross mate, ah sais tae the driver as gob splattered against the side windae.

— Square go then smart cunt! C'moan ya crappin bastards! the shell-suit shouted. The taxi driver wisnae amused. He looked a right cunt. Maist ay them do. The stamp-peyin self-employed ur truly the lowest form ay vermin oan god's earth.

The taxi did a u-turn and sped up the Walk.

— See whit yuv done now, ya big-moothed cunt. Next time one ay us ur walkin hame oan oor Jack Jones, wi git hassle fi these wee radges. Ah wisnae chuffed at Sick Boy.

— Yir no feart ay they wee fuckin saps ur ye?

This cunt's really gittin ma fuckin goat. — Aye! Aye ah fuckin am, if ah'm oan ma tod n ah git set oan by a fuckin squad ay shell-suits! Ye think ah'm Jean-Claude Van Fuckin Damme? Fuckin doss cunt, so ye are Simon. Ah called him 'Simon' rather than 'Si' or 'Sick Boy' tae emphasise the seriousness ay what ah wis sayin.

— Ah want tae see Mother Superior n ah dinnae gie a fuck aboot any cunt or anything else. Goat that? He pokes his lips wi his forefinger, his eyes bulging oot at us. — Simone wants tae see Mother Superior. Watch ma fuckin lips He then turns and stares intae the back ay the taxi driver, willing the cunt tae go faster while nervously beating oot a rhythm oan his thighs.

— One ay they cunts wis a McLean. Dandy n Chancey's wee brar, ah sais.

— Wis it fuck, he sais, but he couldnae keep the anxiety oot ay his voice. — Ah ken the McLeans. Chancey's awright.

— No if ye take the pish oot ay his brar, ah sais.

He wis takin nae mair notice though. Ah stoaped harassing him, knowing thit ah wis jist wastin ma energy. His silent suffering through withdrawal now seemed so intense that thir wis nae wey that ah could add, even incrementally, tae his misery.

From Trainspotting by Irvine Welsh, published by Vintage Books. Reprinted by kind permission of The Random House Group Limited.

CLARA (2002) *by Janice Galloway*
GIRL MEETS BOY (2007) *by Ali Smith*

After the Scotland Act of 1998 and the formation of the Scottish Parliament the following year, this was the first decade since the end of the 17th century in which Scotland was once again a country with its own parliament. Was that reflected in the books its writers were publishing? The answer must be no, unless the impact of greater political autonomy can be read into the increasing confidence and diversity of work being produced. One thing is clear, though: with only a few exceptions – notably James Robertson's novel *And the Land Lay Still* (2010) – politics, of the party kind, have played less of a role in Scotland's literature since Holyrood was established. In its place, there has been a stronger mood of exploration and experimentation. Also of genre writing, especially crime, a market Scotland seems to be cornering with its bare knuckles.

Our choices reflect that broadening outlook. They also reflect the flourishing of women's writing in the past twenty-odd years, which has been one of the welcome features of Scotland's contemporary literary scene. Janice Galloway and Ali Smith are in the premier league of Scottish writing, even though they are still only in the middle of their careers. Galloway came to prominence with her powerful novel, *The Trick is to Keep Breathing*, published in 1989. In the judges' opinion, however, her best work so far has been her extraordinary novel about the pianist Clara Schumann, and her life, first as a prodigy under the iron fist of her ambitious father, and then as wife to a composer whose moods eventually tipped into insanity. Galloway's depiction of Clara's musical genius, and her exhausting shuttle between concert platform and home-front, is a bravura feat of imagination and literary invention.

Ali Smith's novella *Girl Meets Boy* is a reworking of one of Ovid's more upbeat stories of metamorphosis. Smith brings to this bubbly, mischievous romance all the skills that make her a natural short story writer. Her effervescent stream of consciousness style is brilliantly used in this story of a girl who falls in love with a beautiful boy – who looks like a girl. And maybe he is. After all, nothing in this book is as it seems, which is a motif that could stand for all of Smith's quicksilver fictions.

Rarely was the selection process harder than for these years, however. Just thinking about those we did not include is dizzying: we might have selected children's novels by Julie Bertagna (*Exodus*, 2001) and Theresa Breslin (*Remembrance*, 2003). Or such novels as A. L. Kennedy's blisteringly sad and funny *Paradise* (2004), Alan Bissett's rollicking *Boyracers* (2001), Maggie O'Farrell's poignant *After You'd Gone* (2000), Zoë Strachan's worldly and knowing *Negative Space* (2002), Anne Donovan's tender Glasgow story, *Buddha Da* (2003), James Robertson's historical and political novel, *Joseph Knight* (2003), or Louise Welsh's groundbreaking thriller, *The Cutting Room* (2002). The choice was ours, and it was exceedingly tough.

Rosemary Goring,
January 2012

CLARA *by Janice Galloway*

Except for Sunday, which is the Lord's day, mornings are lessons.
Every day the same. Lessons are in the room downstairs, where
other girls take theirs. The *other* girls, that is, the ones who pay. She
waits for him like anyone else in the corner of the stairhead room,
a pupil waiting for her teacher. Which she is. He is. Now. There must
have been a time when music, staved and stuck to the page, was
something unfamiliar. It stands to reason. No one begins with the
page. Yet these seed-pod heads, their sticks and legs, attenuated
hairpins and crack-backed rests have always been there, strewn
on tables and piled in corners, scattered on the music stand where
mother, oozing when her babies cried in other rooms, gave in
and fed them where she sat at the keys. Falling ringlets of stave
brackets, the arcs and bows of phrasings, time signatures, random
confettis of sharps, flats and naturals seemed always to have been
comprehensible; stair runs of semiquavers, no matter how dense,
more loaded with meaning than any alphabet. It's how things are,
have always been.

So is the room in which one waits: familiar, unchanging, known
down to the chips in the painted window ledge. An empty vase, two
candlesticks, a wooden box stuck over with shells, an ornamental
porcelain in the shape of a dancing shoe are the only other things
to see: the same five things on the mantelshelf. And every week, it
seems, she wonders the same five things about them: who it was
that paid money for the useless shoe; why no one misses the vase
for flowers; where the shells have come from, what they are when
they're not stuck to a box, if it's true they're skeletons that once held
their animals inside. Just as she reflects there is nothing interesting
whatsoever about candlesticks, there he is. Punctual. Watching his
watch to prove it. The Mind and the Tree, Clara, he says, opening
the door for her to come in. What do they have in common? She
doesn't know. *They bend*, he whispers. *They bend.* She looks intently
when he tells her here is a new language to learn. French as well as
mother tongue, Italian too – she will not believe how much Italian.
And, of course, singing. Clara, the child who almost never speaks,
tries to think about language, singing. Mother. Tongue. The two
words come easily together for her. She sees how they fit. Her eyes
meet his and lock there, saying it. She understands.

So. Lessons. Practice. Handwriting and study of theory.
Sometimes in the evenings there are house concerts.

She may listen, she may watch, she may sit. Sometimes she may just sit, restraining her extremities as a matter of course. A musician must learn to sit still and expressionless, waiting his or her turn. Grimaces are the province of hopeless amateurs. This is a lesson too. Everything, it seems is lessons. Aphorisms. Notes. Sit still and watch. These are the materials of all learning.

Duty is the Highest Happiness.
Little and Often is the Surest Way.
Play always as if you played for a Master.
Trust God and your Teacher.
The Mind and the Tree etc.

Sometimes lessons were immediately recognisable and open; other times it came about by a kind of stealth. Things that did not seem to be lessons at all at first, would turn out to have a Moral, a Serious Test of Diligence concealed within – a sudden fall or a carriage ride, the apparently unearned offer of a sweet – but Papa was always watching, assessing, noting whether Clara behaved as he would wish. As her Best Self would wish. The mark of the Finest Teacher, he said, is that he Keenly Observes, and he does it a lot. Somewhere in the middle of these early lessons, then, when the talent to observe had become something named and something deliberately to refine, it happened. Something in detail and through the fingers first. An icy bloom under her palm never fails to bring it back, entire: the sensation of looking down from somewhere dizzy. The feeling that at any moment, without warning, she might fall.

From Clara by Janice Galloway, published by Jonathan Cape. Reprinted by kind permission of The Random House Group Limited.

GIRL MEETS BOY *by Ali Smith*

Let me tell you about when I was a girl, our grandfather says.

It is Saturday evening; we always stay at their house on Saturdays. The couch and the chairs are shoved back against the walls. The teak coffee table from the middle of the room is up under the window. The floor has been cleared for the backward and forward somersaults, the juggling with oranges and eggs, the how-to-do-a-cart-wheel, how-to-stand-on-your-head, how-to-walk-on-your-hands lessons. Our grandfather holds us upside-down by the legs until we get our balance. Our grandfather worked in a circus before he met and married our grandmother. He once did headstands on top of a whole troupe of headstanders. He once walked a tightrope across the Thames. The Thames is a river in London, which is five hundred and twenty-seven miles from here, according to the mileage chart in the RAC book in among our father's books at home. Oh, across the Thames, was it? our grandmother says. Not across the falls at Niagara? Ah, Niagara, our grandfather says. Now that was a whole other kittle of fish.

It is after gymnastics and it is before Blind Date. Sometimes after gymnastics it is The Generation Game instead. Back in history The Generation Game was our mother's favourite programme, way before we were born, when she was as small as us. But our mother isn't here any more, and anyway we prefer Blind Date, where every week without fail a boy chooses a girl from three girls and a girl chooses a boy from three boys, with a screen and Cilla Black in between them each time. Then the chosen boys and girls from last week's programme come back and talk about their blind date, which has usually been awful, and there is always excitement about whether there'll be a wedding, which is what it's called before people get divorced, and to which Cilla Black will get to wear a hat.

But which is Cilla Black, then, boy or girl? She doesn't seem to be either. She can look at the boys if she wants; she can go round the screen and look at the girls. She can go between the two sides of things like a magician, or a joke. The audience always laughs with delight when she does it.

You're being ridiculous, Anthea, Midge says shrugging her eyes at me.

Cilla Black is from the sixties, our grandmother says as if that explains everything.

It is Saturday tea-time, after supper and before our bath. It is always exciting to sit in the chairs in the places they usually aren't. Midge and I, one on each knee, are on our grandfather's lap and all three of us are wedged into the pushed-back armchair waiting for our grandmother to settle. She drags her own armchair closer to the electric fire. She puts her whole weight behind the coffee table and shoves it over so she can watch the football results. You don't need the sound up for that. Then she neatens the magazines on the under-rack of the table and then she sits down. Steam rises off teacups. We've got the taste of buttered toast in our mouths. At least, I assume we all have it, since we've all been eating the same toast, well, different bits of the same toast. Then I start to worry. Because what if we all taste things differently? What if each bit of toast tastes completely different? After all, the two bits I've eaten definitely tasted a bit different even from each other. I look round the room, from head to head of each of us. Then I taste the taste in my own mouth again.

So did I never tell you about the time they put me in jail for a week when I was a girl? our grandfather says.

What for? I say.

For saying you were a girl when you weren't one, Midge says.

For writing words, our grandfather says.

What words? I say.

NO VOTES NO GOLF, our grandfather says. They put us in jail because we wrote it into the golf green with acid, me and my friend. What's a young girl like you wanting acid for? the chemist asked me when I went to get it.

Grandad, stop it, Midge says.

What's a girl like you wanting with fifteen bottles of it? he said. I told him the truth, more fool me. I want to write words on the golf course with it, I told him and he sold me it, right enough, but then he went and told Harry Cathcart at the police station exactly who'd been round buying a job lot of acid. We were proud to go to jail, though. I was proud when they came to get me. I said to them all at the police station, I'm doing this because my mother can't write her name with words, never mind vote. Your great-grandmother wrote her name with Xs. X X X. Mary Isobel Gunn.

From Girl Meets Boy by Ali Smith, published by Canongate, and reprinted by kind permission

A LONGLIST OF SCOTTISH WRITING

As Rosemary Goring writes in her introduction, there is no right or wrong top twenty best books for this period and this celebration of Scottish writing highlights a small number from an impressive period.

What do you think? What would you have included? Here's a longlist – by no means comprehensive – of Scottish writers and titles to inspire your own selection!

1911-1919

1911	PETER AND WENDY	J. M. Barrie
1911	FLEMINGTON	Violet Jacob
1911	A SHORT HISTORY OF SCOTLAND	Andrew Lang
1912	THE LOST WORLD	Arthur Conan Doyle
1914	GILLESPIE	John MacDougall Hay
1914	THE NEW ROAD	Neil Munro
1915	THE THIRTY-NINE STEPS	John Buchan
1915	THE FIRST HUNDRED THOUSAND	Ian Hay
1917	ON GROWTH AND FORM	D'Arcy Wentworth Thomson

1920-1929

1920	OPEN THE DOOR!	Catherine Carswell
1920	A VOYAGE TO ARCTURUS	David Lindsay
1922	THE JUDGE	Rebecca West
1922	HUNTINGTOWER	John Buchan
1925	FIRST POEMS	Edwin Muir
1926	A DRUNK MAN LOOKS AT THE THISTLE	Hugh MacDiarmid
1926	DER PUPPENJUNGE	John Henry Mackay
1926	CLOSED DOORS	Annie Shepherd Swan
1927	CALEDONIA: OR THE FUTURE OF THE SCOTS	George Malcolm Thomson
1928	THE QUARRY WOOD	Nan Shepherd
1929	DARK STAR	Lorna Moon

1930-1939

1931	HATTER'S CASTLE	A. J. Cronin
1931	IMAGINED CORNERS	Willa Muir
1931	CONFLICT	William Soutar
1932	SUNSET SONG	Lewis Grassic Gibbon
1933	THE GOWK STORM	Nancy Brysson Morrison
1934	HUNGER MARCH	Dot Allan
1935	THE STARS LOOK DOWN	A. J. Cronin
1935	THE SHIPBUILDERS	George Blake
1935	NO MEAN CITY:A STORY OF THE GLASGOW SLUMS	H. Kingsley Long/ Alexander McArthur
1935	WE HAVE BEEN WARNED	Naomi Mitchison
1935	A SCOTTISH JOURNEY	Edwin Muir
1937	THE CITADEL	A. J. Cronin
1937	HIGHLAND RIVER	Neil M. Gunn
1939	THE NOVEL AND THE MODERN WORLD	David Daiches
1939	THE LAND OF THE LEAL	James Barke

1940-1949

1941	THE SILVER DARLINGS	Neil M. Gunn
1943	DÀIN DO EIMHIR AGUS DÀIN EILE	Somhairle MacGill-Eain
1946	PRIVATE ANGELO	Eric Linklater
1947	FERNIE BRAE	J. F. Hendry
1947	WHISKY GALORE!	Compton Mackenzie
1947	WAX FRUIT	Guy McCrone
1947	THE BULL CALVES	Naomi Mitchison
1948	UNDER THE EILDON TREE	Sidney Goodsir Smith
1948	DANCE OF THE APPRENTICES	Edward Gaitens
1948	ELEGIES FOR THE DEAD IN CYRENAICA	Hamish Henderson

1950-1959

1954	YOUNG ADAM	Alexander Trocchi
1955	THE CONE-GATHERERS	Robin Jenkins
1955	RIDING LIGHTS	Norman MacCaig
1956	TUNES OF GLORY	James Kennaway
1957	FROM RUSSIA WITH LOVE	Ian Fleming
1957	THE GUNS OF NAVARONE	Alistair MacLean
1957	MACGREGOR'S GATHERING	Nigel Tranter
1958	THE CHANGELING	Robin Jenkins
1958	DANCING IN THE STREETS	Cliff Hanley
1958	PARA HANDY TALES	Neil Munro
1958	THE WHITE BIRD PASSES	Jessie Kesson
1959	GOLDFINGER	Ian Fleming
1959	MEMENTO MORI	Muriel Spark

1960-1969

1960	THE DIVIDED SELF	R. D. Laing
1960	RING OF BRIGHT WATER	Gavin Maxwell
1961	THE PRIME OF MISS JEAN BRODIE	Muriel Spark
1961	CULLODEN	John Prebble
1961	CLYDESIDERS	Hugh Munro
1961	THE GAME OF KINGS	Dorothy Dunnett
1964	JERICHO SLEEP ALONE	Chaim Bermant
1964	THE DESPERATE JOURNEY	Kathleen Fidler
1965	A GREEN TREE IN GEDDE	Alan Sharp
1966	THE DEAR GREEN PLACE	Archie Hind
1966	SURROUNDINGS	Norman MacCaig
1968	CONSIDER THE LILIES	Iain Crichton Smith
1968	THE SECOND LIFE	Edwin Morgan
1969	A HISTORY OF THE SCOTTISH PEOPLE 1560-1830	T. C. Smout
1969	THE SIEGE OF TRENCHER'S FARM	Gordon Williams

1970-1979

1970	FERGUS LAMONT	Robin Jenkins
1970	THE DRIVER'S SEAT	Muriel Spark
1971	CREATING A SCENE	Elspeth Davie
1972	ACROSS THE BARRICADES	Joan Lingard
1972	GREENVOE	George Mackay Brown
1972	GLASGOW SONNETS	Edwin Morgan
1972	MR ALFRED, M.A.	George Friel
1972	THE BREADMAKERS	Margaret Thomson Davis
1973	FROM GLASGOW TO SATURN	Edwin Morgan
1973	MY SCOTLAND: FRAGMENTS OF A STATE OF MIND	George MacBeth
1974	LOVE OR NOTHING	Douglas Dunn
1975	DOCHERTY	William McIlvanney
1975	TWO MEN AND A BLANKET: MEMOIRS OF CAPTIVITY	Robert Garioch
1976	GLASGOW POEMS	Tom Leonard
1976	THE HIGH TIDE TALKER	Elspeth Davie
1977	A SENSE OF FREEDOM	Jimmy Boyle
1977	LAIDLAW	William McIlvanney
1977	ITS COLOURS THEY ARE FINE	Alan Spence
1977	THE BREAK-UP OF BRITAIN: CRISIS AND NEO-NATIONALISM	Tom Nairn
1978	WILD MOUNTAIN THYME	Rosamunde Pilcher
1978	DEVIL IN THE DARKNESS	Archie Roy

1980-1989

1981	LANARK: A LIFE IN FOUR BOOKS	Alasdair Gray
1981	MURDO	Iain Crichton Smith
1984	THE WASP FACTORY	Iain Banks
1984	BROND	Frederic Lindsay
1984	THE BUSCONDUCTOR HINES	James Kelman
1984	1982, JANINE	Alasdair Gray
1984	DREAMING FRANKENSTEIN	Liz Lochhead
1984	INTIMATE VOICES	Tom Leonard
1985	A TWELVEMONTH AND A DAY	Christopher Rush
1986	GROWING UP IN THE GORBALS	Ralph Glasser
1986	GRUTS	Ivor Cutler
1986	ELVIS IS DEAD	Carl McDougall
1986	QUEST FOR A KELPIE	Frances Mary Hendry
1987	THE SHELL SEEKERS	Rosamunde Pilcher
1987	THE SOUND OF MY VOICE	Ron Butlin
1987	MADAME DOUBTFIRE	Anne Fine
1989	A QUESTION OF LOYALTIES	Allan Massie
1989	THE TRICK IS TO KEEP BREATHING	Janice Galloway

1990-1999

1990	RADICAL RENFREW	Tom Leonard
1990	THE MAGIC FLUTE	Alan Spence
1992	ELECTRIC BRAE	Andrew Greig
1992	SWING HAMMER SWING!	Jeff Torrington
1992	THE CROW ROAD	Iain Banks
1992	POOR THINGS	Alasdair Gray
1993	TRAINSPOTTING	Irvine Welsh
1993	NIL, NIL	Don Paterson
1994	DEBATABLE LAND	Candia McWilliam
1994	HOW LATE IT WAS, HOW LATE	James Kelman
1994	MUSIC IN A FOREIGN LANGUAGE	Andrew Crumey
1994	SOMETHING VERY LIKE MURDER	Frank Kuppner
1995	MORVERN CALLAR	Alan Warner
1995	BEHIND THE SCENES AT THE MUSEUM	Kate Atkinson
1995	SO I AM GLAD	A. L. Kennedy
1995	MEALL GARBH	Derick Thomson
1995	THE MERMAIDS SINGING	Val McDermid
1995	THE ORCHARD ON FIRE	Shena Mackay
1995	DRIVETIME	James Meek
1995	THE MISSING	Andrew O'Hagan
1996	QUITE UGLY ONE MORNING	Christopher Brookmyre
1997	GRACE NOTES	Bernard MacLaverty
1997	BLACK AND BLUE	Ian Rankin
1997	HARRY POTTER AND THE PHILOSOPHER'S STONE	J. K. Rowling
1998	FOR THE LOVE OF WILLIE	Agnes Owens
1998	TRUMPET	Jackie Kay
1998	GARNETHILL	Denise Mina
1998	JELLY ROLL	Luke Sutherland
1999	THE WORLD'S WIFE	Carol Ann Duffy
1999	JIZZEN	Kathleen Jamie
1999	BORN FREE	Laura Hird
1999	THE LANTERN BEARERS	Ronald Frame
1999	THE LIGHTHOUSE STEVENSONS	Bella Bathurst
1999	OUR FATHERS	Andrew O'Hagan
1999	NO GREAT MISCHIEF	Alastair MacLeod
1999	THE SCOTTISH NATION: 1700-2000	Tom Devine

2000-2011

2000	THE SEA ROAD	Margaret Elphinstone
2000	UNDER THE SKIN	Michel Faber
2000	AFTER YOU'D GONE	Maggie O'Farrell
2001	IN THE BLUE HOUSE	Meaghan Delahunt
2001	THE DARK SHIP	Anne MacLeod
2001	HOTEL WORLD	Ali Smith
2001	GLUE	Irvine Welsh
2001	BOYRACERS	Alan Bissett
2001	BLUE POPPIES	Jonathan Falla
2002	EXODUS	Julie Bertagna
2002	CLARA	Janice Galloway
2002	THE CRIMSON PETAL AND THE WHITE	Michel Faber
2002	STONE VOICES: THE SEARCH FOR SCOTLAND	Neal Ascherson
2002	NEGATIVE SPACE	Zoë Strachan
2002	THE CUTTING ROOM	Louise Welsh
2002	REMEMBRANCE	Theresa Breslin
2003	AN OIDHCHE MUS DO SHEÒL SINN	AONGHAS Pàdraig Caimbeul
2003	DRIFTNET	Lin Anderson
2003	SCABBIT ISLAND	Tom Pow
2003	BUDDHA DA	Anne Donovan
2004	JOSEPH KNIGHT	James Robertson
2004	PARADISE	A. L. Kennedy
2004	PSYCHORAAG	Suhayl Saadi
2005	THE ACCIDENTAL	Ali Smith
2006	THE TESTAMENT OF GIDEON MACK	James Robertson
2006	SCOTS: THE MITHER TONGUE	Billy Kay
2007	GIRL MEETS BOY	Ali Smith
2009	RAIN	Don Paterson
2010	KICK-ASS	Mark Millar
2010	AND THE LAND LAY STILL	James Robertson
2010	BEYOND THE LAST DRAGON	James McDonigal
2010	A LIFE IN PICTURES	Alasdair Gray
2010	RED DUST ROAD	Jackie Kay
2010	THE BREAKFAST ROOM	Stewart Conn
2010	WHAT TO LOOK FOR IN WINTER	Candia McWilliam

2011	CIVILISATION: THE WEST AND THE REST	Niall Ferguson
2011	TO THE ENDS OF THE EARTH: SCOTLAND'S GLOBAL DIASPORA	Tom Devine
2011	THE BLUE BOOK	A. L. Kennedy
2011	THERE BUT FOR THE	Ali Smith
2011	BLACK CAT BONE	John Burnside